ACHMELVICH BEACH, ASSYNT : J. CAMPBELL KERR.

People's Friend An

Contents

Complete Stories

p6

p34

p104

p11

Old Country Life

p29

Poetry by Brenda G. Macrow

J. Campbell Kerr Paintings

p32

p141

p94

Dear Reader,

Happy new year and a warm welcome to the "Friend" Annual for 2001.

We're pleased to bring you a brand new selection of heartwarming Stories by favourite "Friend" writers to take you through the year ahead.

You'll also be able to enjoy a taste of Scotland's islands in a special series of features. Take a trip down the years with poet Brenda G. Macrow as she reflects on old country living. And discover charming paintings from around Britain by "Friend" cover artist J. Campbell Kerr.

Whether you enjoy romance, nostalgia, humour or family Stories to touch your heart, you'll find hours of great reading in this colourful Annual.

The Editor

p57

A Taste Of Scotland's Islands

Illustration by John Hancock.

F LORA MILLIGAN sat beside her
boyfriend Alex in the plane, nervously
clutching his hand.

It wasn't flying she was nervous about; she'd done her share of
that in her twenty-two years. No — this was the first time she'd taken
Alex home, to the island where she was brought up. And it was the first
time she'd brought a boyfriend — any boyfriend — to meet her parents.

She so wanted Alex to be impressed by the beauty and magic of her
homeland and love it as much as she did. Her parents' cottage was at the
edge of a small village just a stone's throw from the sea; you'd be hard
pushed to find a more idyllic spot. But would it appeal to Alex?

He was always so smart and so well dressed. The city suited him as
much as he suited the city, with his grey eyes and easy grace.

Sometimes she wondered if she was a bit much for the civilised Alex.

A Different Sort Of Holiday

by Sylvia Wynne.

They worked in the same office, and had been drawn to each other after a colleague's birthday party, when they'd danced with no-one else all evening.

"It's fairly primitive at home," Flora now warned him. "Not a computer or fax in sight!"

"I'm sure it'll be marvellous!" He squeezed her hand. "I'm really looking forward to it."

Flora hoped beyond hope that it wouldn't rain all the time. She cast her mind back to her childhood, but like most memories, the days were sun-filled and shower free.

They arrived safely at the small island airport and Flora breathed in the sharp northern air, revelling in it after the city fumes. Alex, however, huddled into his smart jacket.

"Bit chilly, isn't it?"

"It's wonderful!" Flora exulted. "Just you wait till you've run up the mountain and back tomorrow to give you an appetite for breakfast!"

Alex laughed nervously, and his query about whether or not she was actually serious was lost in her parents' hugs and greetings.

"It's lovely to meet you at last," Ailsa, Flora's mum, assured Alex. "Come on, we'll get you back to the cottage — you look like you could do with a hot cup of coffee!"

LATER, when they'd unpacked, Flora suggested they went down for a stroll along the beach.

"Cold enough for you?" she asked as they fought their way along the wide pebbly strand against a buffeting wind.

"It's freezing!" he shouted above the noise of the wind and the waves. "Is it always as cold as this?"

"It's October! You should have taken the offer of Dad's windproof jacket." She hugged him closer to her, hoping to transfer some of her enthusiasm and warmth to him. What if he was secretly wondering how he was going to survive the weekend? There was nothing much to do but huddle over the fire or brave the elements . . . and she really didn't want to spend the entire holiday watching TV!

By the time they got back to the cottage, the wind had really got up.

"There'll be a few tiles flying off roofs tonight!" John, Flora's father, remarked with a cheery grin.

As he spoke, the lights went out and they were plunged into darkness. Their surprised faces were illuminated by the glow of the fire.

"Is it a fuse? Can I help?" Alex offered shyly.

"That's no fuse," John said grimly. He'd gone over to peer out from behind the window curtain.

"There are no lights anywhere. Looks like it's a power-cut."

They listened to news flashes on the old battery transistor radio Flora had left in her room when she went to London. It seemed that the gales had brought down several power lines and it would be hours before they were put right.

Ailsa found candles, and John got Alex to help him bring in wood from the pile stacked against the house.

"It's spooky!" Flora laughed, quite excited by the power-cut. "I remember hoping the cuts would last into the next day, so as we could miss school!" She turned to smile at Alex, knowing that this was, for him, a first. But as the firelight threw flickering shadows on to their faces, she could see he looked strained. Her heart sank.

Perhaps he didn't see it as an exciting adventure. Had she been wrong to invite him here? But it was so important that he saw and understood this place that meant so much to her, that was a part of her.

Ailsa boiled up water in a pan over the fire for a late night cup of tea, but washing had to be done in cold water and in the dark.

Flora snuggled into bed, happy to be home. But the wind still gusted round the house, and she wondered how Alex was getting on in the room next door.

She was fast asleep when she heard his voice confusedly through her dream.

"Are you awake, Flora?"

She could just discern his face looming above hers in the dim light from the window.

She sat up in bed.

"Oh, Alex!" Sleepily, she rubbed her eyes. "Can't you sleep?"

"It's quieter than the city, but somehow it's noisier, too!"

Pulling her duvet round her, Flora swung her legs out of bed.

"Let's go downstairs and see if there's any heat left in the fire."

Huddled in their quilts on the rug before the hearth, they coaxed the warm embers with kindling into a nice little blaze. Flora had found a brick in the scullery, and they pushed it into the ashes.

"My gran said they used to heat bricks in the olden days. They'd wrap them in bits of blanket to warm their feet in bed."

She saw Alex smile in the firelight.

"They didn't set their bedclothes alight?"

"It wasn't that hot, silly!" She leaned against him drowsily. "Warming up?"

"This is nice!" Alex murmured.

They were quite content sitting together, blinking into the flames, chatting about this and that — their memories, their hopes for the future . . . Flora realised she'd never have learnt this much about Alex in any other circumstances, and it occurred to Alex as he gazed into the embers, that there was nowhere he'd rather be than here with Flora.

Finally they stumbled back upstairs to bed, him hugging the warm brick wrapped in a piece of old sheet.

"I'll sleep now," he told her, and reached forward to give her a sweet, warm, lingering kiss before going back to his room.

Flora meant to lie awake and think about what had happened, go over their closeness in her mind, luxuriating in the memory. But she closed her eyes, and before she knew it, it was morning.

Light was filtering through the curtains, as a surge of wonderful love filled her. Scrambling out of bed, she went and knocked on Alex's door, peering round it.

"Come on, sleepyhead — breakfast time!"

His eyes met hers above the duvet.

"That brick did the trick. I went out like a light!"

Going downstairs, they found Ailsa busy with kindling at the fire, while John brought in logs.

"Still no power. How did you two sleep?"

Herdwick sheep in the Langdale Valley.

"Like bricks!" they chorused together and Ailsa raised a quizzical eyebrow.

Flora opened the back door, and cold air rushed in. Though the wind had dropped, the blue sky was cloudless, and there was a sharp nip in the air.

Alex shuddered.

"It doesn't get any warmer!"

She put an arm round him. He was shaggy-haired, red-nosed,

The Good Shepherd

WITH faithful dogs, he guards his flock
Against the birds of prey;
The hungry fox that comes to steal
A lamb by night or day.

And on his croft when wintry winds
Blow cold around the byre,
He bottle-feeds the orphan lambs
Beside the kitchen fire.

With shearing, dipping, sales, he works
All hours beneath the sun,
Till lambing time comes round again —
His task is never done.

An ancient craft the shepherd plies,
Its roots are buried deep.
And often is the human race
Identified with sheep

Like sheep, we, too, may go astray
Until, with love serene,
Our Shepherd leads us home again
To dwell in pastures green.

And shepherds down the ages still
This old tradition keep,
And brave all perils on the hill
To saved one stranded sheep.
— *Brenda G. Macrow.*

T. Parker.

unshaven, but she loved him!

"Wait till you get outside a bowl of Mum's porridge!"

"Shall I give you a hand with those logs, Mr Milligan?"

"That would be grand, Alex — and do call me John."

Flora could hear the men laughing as they brought logs from the barn to the lean-to by the house.

"*Well*, Mum? What d'you think of him?" Flora asked casually.

"He seems a nice enough boy," returned Ailsa, cautious as she tended

11

to be where her daughter's feelings were concerned. "He's not really used to our ways, though, is he?"

"Oh, *Mum!* Who could expect a power-cut?" Flora protested. "It's enough to put anyone off."

"There's a bit of colour in your cheeks, now, Alex," Ailsa noticed as the men came back indoors.

Alex rubbed his hands together, standing by the now blazing fire. "Gosh, the sea's wild, isn't it?"

"Aye, we should go down before lunch and watch the white horses coming in."

At Alex's bewilderment, they all laughed. Flora only hoped they weren't overdoing the outdoor bit. Maybe Alex would rather stay in by the fire?

However, he came along with them without protest, this time accepting John's offer of an extra jacket. The waves were indeed rolling in down on the shore, the sea was still boiling from yesterday's gales and spindrift was flying on the freshening breeze.

"Goodness!" Alex laughed into the wind. "To think people bother with the Costa Brava!"

As they came up the lane, lights suddenly sprang up in all the houses. "Look!" Ailsa cried. "The power's on again!"

"I was looking forward to another candle-lit supper!" Alex laughed.

IT'S gone so fast, Flora thought sadly as, bags at their feet, they queued at the airport for the return flight the next morning. Visitors had called in the night before and stayed late, and to her frustration, she and Alex hadn't had a chance to be on their own.

She hoped the cold, the bracing walks and the local gossip hadn't been too much for him. It was so different from anything he was accustomed to.

"It's been a funny sort of a holiday, I'm afraid," Ailsa apologised. "I don't know what you must have thought of us, Alex."

Flora waited for the tactful disclaimers.

However, Alex turned a glowing face to her.

"It's been totally brilliant — the best holiday I've ever had, Ailsa!" And there was no doubting the sincerity in his voice.

"You must come again. But I'm afraid we can't arrange a power-cut every time!" John Milligan smiled.

"All the same, try and keep me away!" Alex laughed, and gave Ailsa a warm kiss and a hug, and shook John's hand.

And Flora realised this was only the first of many visits. Of course Alex found the island as wonderful as she did. Just as he'd revealed the marvels of the city to her, she had introduced him to the island way.

She couldn't wait to get on the plane and go over the whole splendid weekend with him, hour by hour! And start planning the next one! ■

by Barbara Povey.

Illustration by Sally Rowe.

Amazing Grace!

GRACE strode through the open gates of Billington Park, swinging her bag of library books and revelling in the autumn sunshine.

With luck, she'd find her special bench vacant. Then she'd enjoy an hour in the fresh air, escaping into the cloak-and-dagger world of her favourite author.

She paused, briefly, to watch a group of schoolgirls in red sweatshirts and shorts playing football with energy and expertise. How different from her own schooldays!

She would have loved to race across the grass, kicking a ball vigorously. She would have been a good player! She was tall and well built and would have been quite at home on a football pitch.

She hadn't been any good at hockey. She shuddered to think of her attempts to control that hard little ball with the inflexible stick.

Tennis was even worse.

"Completely lacking in co-ordination," the games mistress decided. "No ball skills whatsoever."

But a *football* — that was different! Being so tall, she'd have had the advantage of her size and reach in goal. That would have been something else!

Grace walked on, deep in thought, past the Victorian drinking fountain, now long unused. In her youth there had been a heavy beaker secured to the fountain by a length of chain. How cold and clean the water had tasted . . .

She rounded the pond, where ducks squabbled noisily over bread crusts which littered the water. Young mothers in their colourful, casual clothes chattered brightly round a cluster of buggies.

Grace recalled the uniformed nannies with their shiny, black prams walking briskly round the park on their daily constitutional. How times had changed, she thought again.

Beyond the duckpond and through a rustic arch, Grace entered the formal rose garden surrounded by a high beech hedge. A place of privacy and peace where a few late roses perfumed the air.

Good! Only one bench occupied and by the gentleman who always remained hidden behind his newspaper, discouraging any attempts at conversation.

"Lovely morning," Grace remarked politely, as she passed to the bench in the far corner.

"Grummmph!" he retorted.

Grace could live with that. A normal Saturday morning.

Placing her bag of books beside her, she removed her gloves, loosened her jacket and raised her face to the warmth of the October sun.

S HE was content. Life had not followed the prescribed course of the stories in women's magazines, but she was happy with her lot. The trouble had been that Grace, in spite of her name, was not a graceful, or feminine, woman. And in her young days, women had been expected to be feminine.

Tall, big-boned and inclined to be clumsy, that was how she was — but she'd learned, at an early age, to make the best of reality and not waste time dreaming of what might have been.

All those years at the Bon Marché had done nothing to soften or polish Grace. Nearly half a century and she'd never progressed beyond "Haberdashery".

Though not unhappy in her work, there had been times when she'd longed to handle the beautiful materials in "Gowns"; the silks and satins of "Lingerie", or the flowers and frippery of "Millinery".

Fate, and Mr Edwards of Personnel, had decreed that she could do least harm in haberdashery and there she'd stayed, counting out buttons and curtain hooks; measuring lengths of petersham and matching sewing threads to fabrics. Her fingers had felt like so many thumbs, but she'd coped.

But now she was free! No more nine-to-six, Monday to Saturday. Her pension was meagre, but her tastes were modest.

Life was good.

She opened her eyes quickly at the sound of a rustle and whoosh. Through the topmost twigs of the tall beech hedge, a black and white football shot like a cannon ball.

Instinctively, Grace leapt to her feet and caught the missile in her large, capable hands.

What sounded remarkably like a chuckle came from behind the newspaper. Grace stood, uncertain, waiting to see what happened next.

She hadn't long to wait. Around the corner of the hedge appeared a skinny boy, his freckled face wearing a worried frown.

On spotting the football, he heaved a sigh of relief.

"That's my football! Sorry — didn't mean to kick it so hard!" He held out his hands, claiming ownership.

"You should be on the other side of the park, in the games area. No balls allowed in here," Grace admonished, but her smile softened the reprimand.

"I know. I know, but . . ." He seemed to be seeking a plausible excuse. "Did *you* catch it?" He changed tack.

"Yes. In time to save the rose bushes." She handed over the ball.

He stared with admiration at Grace's hands.

"Great hands! Goalie's hands!" He nodded his head approvingly.

"Thank you!" Grace was not quite sure how to react to the compliment and was further disconcerted by the newspaper which appeared to be shaking uncontrollably.

The young boy's earnest blue eyes gazed up into Grace's face.

"Fancy a game now? Just shooting in. You in goals," he inquired.

"Well, I . . . I've never actually played . . ." she began.

"Come on, then!"

Suddenly she found herself following the ball and its owner round the far side of the beech hedge and on to a threadbare patch of turf.

Within seconds, she was positioned between a discarded shabby anorak and a grey woollen scarf.

After a few shots at the makeshift goal and three comfortable saves by the novice goalkeeper, the boy approached her, holding out a grubby hand.

"I'm Byron," he informed her. And, by way of explanation, "My mum likes poetry."

"Grace," she responded.

He thought this information through for a minute.

"That's no good for a footballer! Have you got another name?"

Having to admit to being Grace was bad enough, there was no way she was going to add Felicity.

"Dalglish. Miss Dalglish." She must try to salvage some dignity from this bizarre situation.

Byron beamed approvingly.

A Taste Of

I NEVER tire of visiting this beautiful island. Its rugged mountains, glens and coastal villages support a population of over 4000 people — and how I wish I was one of them!

Thanks to the island's proud history of self-sufficiency, everything on Arran has its own unique flavour.

The Blackfaced sheep dot the landscape, munching their way through a rich and varied diet on the hills and moors. Arran lamb is prized for its sweetness.

Beef on Arran is varied, but it retains the character of the native Scottish breeds, such as Aberdeen Angus and Luing.

The island's milk — which isn't used for making the famous Arran cheese — is pasteurised at Arran Dairies, in Brodick. I always feel I have been transported back to my childhood when I see how the rich milk has formed an old-fashioned cream line on the bottles . . .

Sadly, fishing on Arran has declined steadily since the 19th century. A number of lobster fishermen command high prices for their catch, however, and other shellfish, such as whelks and razor-fish, can still be had.

The end of September is the prime time for a visit if you're a bramble fan. Arran is specially famous for its wild brambles, and picking excursions reach a peak at this time. Other soft fruits, such as raspberries and strawberries, are grown commercially at Whiting Bay.

The Arran potato has an interesting history. Lamlash shopkeeper Donald McKelvie made Arran potatoes famous when his first variety, Arran Chief, appeared in 1911. Although McKelvie's varieties have long since been surpassed by new ones, you'll still find locally grown potatoes in shops, where they're labelled with a special tag.

The modern factory plant of Arran Fine Foods in Lamlash is well worth a visit — but remember to take a large shopping bag! Following a visit to this shop, I usually have

"Dalglish. Great! I'll call you Kenny. Come on, Kenny. Two more shots then I must go."

Grace dutifully saved his best efforts and retired, out of breath and slightly dishevelled, to her bench in the rose garden.

Her cheeks were pink with exertion and the glow spread right through her body. She felt really alive.

The taciturn gentleman folded his newspaper neatly and rose from his seat.

"Well done!" he murmured as he passed by.

Good gracious! Whatever next, Grace thought, the pink flush deepening to crimson.

Twice during the following week Grace took a stroll through the park and rested for a while on her favourite bench. Neither Byron nor the newspaper reader made an appearance.

The following Saturday, autumn suddenly decided to become winter. Early frost ravaged the dahlias and cruel winds reduced

Gordon Henderson.

Glen Sannox, Arran.

enough jams, marmalades, relishes and mustards to last at least a year! These traditional preserves, based on old family recipes, are simply irresistible!

For those with a weakness for the sweeter things in life, there are also a few small domestic sweetie producers, who sell their tablet and fudge to the larger commercial concern, The Arran Sweetie Kitchen in Brodick. Dieters beware!

There's no better way to finish off a culinary tour than with a visit to The Arran Malt, set in beautiful surroundings at Lochranza. The whisky, with its peaty aroma, truly captures the flavour of this magical island.

the roses to pot-pourri.

Grace decided to sit for just five minutes in the park then return home to the warmth and comfort of her cosy kitchen.

As she glanced down at her watch, she missed Byron's slight figure coming through the rustic arch. His cotton shorts and thin anorak weren't protection against the winter chill.

"Hi, Kenny! Can't play today. Sorry," he apologised.

Grace looked down with concern at the pale, pinched face, and the hands blue with cold. Then she realised his right hand clutched one end of a piece of string — the other end being attached to an extremely shaggy hearthrug. On closer inspection, the hearthrug proved to be a dog.

"It's Albert, see. Got to find a home for Albert. I thought he could live with us, you know, outside in the yard, but Mum says it's too cold and the neighbours wouldn't like it."

He patted the head of the hearthrug dog, which gazed back at him with adoration in its melting brown eyes.

"Costs too much to feed as well. Me and mum being on our own. Well, us and Keats — he's my baby brother."

Well, it could have been worse, Grace told herself, thinking of Tennyson and Wordsworth.

Then she realised Byron was regarding her with a very serious expression, as if somehow she would find a solution to his problem.

"Oh, dear," she began.

"Have you got a dog, Kenny?" he asked eagerly.

"Er, no," Grace answered briefly, a germ of suspicion beginning to grow in her mind.

"A cat?"

"No. No dog or cat."

"Well, there you are then." Byron was satisfied. Problem solved.

With as much ceremony as if handing over the crown jewels, he placed the dirty piece of string into Grace's hand.

"Don't overfeed him. He's a greedy little thing."

"Oh, no! Come back! I can't . . ." Grace's voice rose in panic but, with utmost confidence in her ability to cope, Byron had vanished round the corner of the beech hedge.

"No dogs allowed unless on a lead," a deep voice commented.

"It is on a . . . Well, on a string," Grace countered lamely, but Mr Newspaper had a smile on his face.

"Had her long? What's her name?" he asked, bending down to give the shaggy creature a friendly pat.

"It's not actually mine and its name is Albert."

"Oh! Funny name for a lady dog."

"A lady dog?" Grace gasped and stepped back until the string was at full stretch.

Albert moved closer and sat down neatly at Grace's feet, gazing up with the same adoring expression she had employed with Byron.

Grace bent and smoothed the tangled hair on Albert's head. The warmth brought a tenderness to her whole being.

She had always wanted a dog. A dog of her own to walk over the common . . .

But first, she had to get Albert home. A bath, first . . . then brush and groom. And nourishing food, of course.

She pictured the two of them resting in front of her welcoming coal fire.

"You'll have to change her name," the newspaper man suggested.

"No. I think not," Grace decided. After all, she herself had been misnamed for sixty years and "Albert" had a nice, comfortable ring to it.

"I've a good leather collar and lead at home," the newspaper man was saying. "I've no use for them now — I'll bring them here tomorrow."

He smiled, a friendly, see-you-again smile, as he strolled away without waiting for Grace's reply.

He really did have a very pleasant voice . . . ∎

BEST FOOT FORWARD

by Barbara Hallihan.

JENNY MARSDEN hurried along with everyone else. She didn't
need to, but it seemed bad manners not to do what everyone else
did in the town.

She'd left her flat in good time, as usual. She lived alone, so
there was no-one to upset her morning routine. And her flat was still
quite bare, as she'd only been living there for three weeks. Once she'd
had breakfast, there was nothing else to do but go out to work.

She looked around at all the people hurrying to work, desperately wanting to see a face she knew. Yet, she knew she wouldn't — she was still a stranger here.

Her roaming eyes were caught by a window display in a large department store, and she stopped abruptly, causing the woman behind to bump into her. She apologised absent-mindedly, her eyes still fixed on the window.

What had caught her attention was the display — a representation of an open-air café in a continental city. Mannequins were sitting at tables and, at one, a waiter was leaning over, as if to serve wine to a woman sitting alone.

Jenny knew that these were artificial figures, but there seemed to be a wistful expression on the face of the woman at the table. The figure was sitting in a listless attitude, her beautiful peacock-blue silk skirt trailing on the ground as she leaned on one elbow, looking into the wine glass.

She looks like I feel, Jenny thought sadly.

A push-chair wheel across her ankle pulled her out of her reverie with an anguished squawk. The push-chair owner, a harassed-looking young woman, barely looked at Jenny as she swerved the chair away.

Once in the office at the carpet store where she worked, Jenny pulled her trouser leg up and rolled her sock down. She saw that the push-chair had actually cut her. Her ankle was bleeding quite badly — and it was starting to throb painfully.

LOOKS like somebody kicked you for saying the wrong thing," a quiet voice said.

Jenny looked up to see a young man gazing down at her. She didn't know his name but had seen him in the shop a few times. She knew he worked in one of the offices.

His dark brown eyes looked at her sympathetically.

"It is very sore," she admitted. "I'd better go and buy a new pair of socks and clean up."

"Mm." The silence which followed was awkward and then he spoke in a rush.

"If it's as sore as it looks, shall I go? That is, if you'd trust me. I know where you can get socks . . ." He was looking at her hopefully.

"Thank you, er —"

"Gordon, Gordon Salinger. I work in the accounts office."

He wasn't five minutes and was soon dropping a small parcel on to her desk with a wink.

"Hope you like them," he said, before he rushed back to his office.

As she was locking up to go home that night, Jenny looked out for Gordon, hoping to thank him, but she only saw him briefly, before he shot off to catch his bus.

Jenny stopped at the shop window again on her way home. The model was still staring into her wine glass, and the waiter still waiting to pour.

Her sad expression made her seem so isolated from the brightness of the scene around her.

Jenny wandered home slowly, trying to put off the moment when the door would shut behind her and cut her off from the rest of the human race. As she prepared pasta for her meal, she reached a decision.

She must snap out of her loneliness — she was being a wimp. Wimps didn't get anywhere. She'd moved to a new job and a new city, now she'd have to find some new friends. After all, that's what independent women do.

DURING a quiet moment next day, Jenny got the staff directory out of her desk drawer and found the number for the accounts office. "Hello, Gordon, it's the sock woman." She felt silly as soon as the words were out, but his gentle laugh put her at ease.

"Hi. I hope those socks weren't too bright for you?"

"Oh, they were fine. In fact, I think neon pink may be my colour."

He laughed with her.

"Look, er — are you free this evening?" Jenny tried to keep her voice calm.

"I'm afraid not. It's my Dutch night."

"Pardon?"

"My Dutch night. I'm learning it at evening classes. Why?"

Why? Because she wanted to see him again, that's why. She took a deep breath, determined not to be put off.

"Because I'd like to thank you for the socks — maybe buy you a coffee."

"That'd be lovely. Could you make it Thursday?"

"Yes, yes I could."

"So where shall we go?"

He made it all so easy and straightforward that Jenny forgot her shyness. The arrangements were soon made.

That night after work, there was a lift in her step, in spite of her sore ankle. This evening was different, even though it was Gordon's Dutch night, and she was going home alone again.

She stopped at the window, this time to look at the rest of the café. She would like to go with Gordon to a place like that. Her thoughts raced ahead. Perhaps they had cafés like that in Holland and they could make it a Dutch day, or week, or whatever.

There was something different here today, too. Someone had been changing the display. The peacock-blue skirt still trailed over the long legs, but now the model was leaning back in her chair, and had moved her glass nearer the waiter.

Jenny stared at her. The model's face seemed happier somehow. Her lips were lifted at the corners and the eyes were smiling. And, suddenly, Jenny realised she was smiling, too. ■

It's N

LIZZIE gazed around the station for the umpteenth time and then stole a glance at her watch yet again. Jon was now twenty minutes late . . .

Perhaps he wasn't coming, after all. She decided she'd wait until the full half-hour was up and then leave.

She tweaked her jacket rather self-consciously. She'd chosen this suit in the hope it would make her appear sophisticated; show him she was no longer the scatty do-gooder he'd left behind.

She looked down at the silk rosebud in her hand, feeling suddenly foolish. She'd been so flattered when he'd suggested they meet here — underneath the station clock. It showed he hadn't forgotten her affection for old romantic Noël Coward films.

She'd thought the rose, which he'd given her early on in their romance, would be a fitting gesture on her part. But she was beginning to regret her impulsive action, as he probably was his.

• • • • • • • • • • **by Julie McGowan.** • • • • • • • • • •

Jon had liked her sentimental side when they'd first met. She'd been a student nurse then, cramming for her finals, while he studied law and politics and took full advantage of the hectic social life London provided.

He'd laughed indulgently at her capacity to always be on hand when calamity struck someone, always willing to help out.

"It's lucky nurses don't wear those capes any more, or Batman would have a run for his money," he'd teased affectionately.

It had been just such an occasion which had brought them together. Stepping heedlessly out into a busy street, Jon had been knocked over by a passing cyclist. Lizzie had happened to be nearby and he'd found capable hands tending his cuts and grazes, while a gentle, soothing voice assured him there was no serious damage done.

"I think such a pretty rescuer deserves a coffee," he'd said. Coffee had extended into lunch and then a film date for the next evening. Soon

they'd started dating regularly.

They found a jazz and folk club in a basement off the Charing Cross Road, where Jon would sit and watch the different emotions flit across her face as she listened to some woeful ballad. And she, in turn, would gaze in admiration when they sat late into the long summer evenings, outside a riverside pub, while Jon became embroiled in some lengthy political debate with his fellow students.

But, eventually, the things which had attracted them to one another in the first place began to drive them apart. Jon's busy social life didn't always fit in with Lizzie's demanding shifts as a newly-qualified staff nurse. He was often very late for their dates — they never had any time to relax together. She couldn't help becoming annoyed when he spent more time at meetings than he did with her.

Yet Lizzie had her own weaknesses. Her collection of "waifs and strays" often got in the way of their plans. Once it was the young girl she'd met busking outside the tube station. Lizzie had insisted on taking her back to her flat for a good meal — then the girl had departed with the contents of Lizzie's savings jar! Another time there'd been the old lady who'd asked them the way to a department store while they were Christmas shopping. Lizzie had insisted on accompanying her, with Jon trailing along, muttering about the time.

"You always put other people first. We never have any time together!" he'd complained.

"But it's all right if it's your career, or your life, interfering with our plans, isn't it?" she'd retorted hotly.

And then there were her parents. She insisted on returning home on her days off. Being the "last-minute miracle" of middle-aged parents, her father was already retired when she began her training. Her parents were very proud of her and Lizzie loved to spend time with them.

"You have to cut the apron strings sometime!" an exasperated Jon finally exclaimed.

His own parents had energetically flung three sons and a daughter from the nest and now travelled the world golfing! How could he understand the bond between Lizzie and her mum and dad?

The crunch came, as deep down she'd known it would, when his brilliant honours degree won him the offer of a job in America.

"Come live with me and be my love!" he gaily quoted at her. "It's the opportunity of a lifetime — a five-year contract — you must come with me!" He'd never seemed so wonderful as he did then, his face shining with optimism.

"I can't," she'd whispered painfully. "I can't leave. What about Mum . . .?" Her mother had been unwell for some time.

There'd been a letter or two from him once he'd gone, but she hadn't replied. It didn't seem fair somehow.

It's Never Too Late

JON sat on the edge of his seat in the taxi, willing it to go faster. He hadn't realised how much busier the London streets had become in the few years he'd been away. He'd wanted to be on time, to please her; show her how much this meeting meant to him. But he was nearly half an hour late already. Would she still be waiting for him?

He should have waited for her five years ago — he knew that now. There would have been other jobs, other opportunities. But then it had seemed as if there was so little time, life had to be grabbed in case it went by too quickly.

His priorities had changed when his father had needed him suddenly and a blizzard had closed the airport so he couldn't get home.

"I should've been there," he'd told his new American friends. "I never had time to talk to him properly."

They had sympathised, but he knew that Lizzie would have understood so much better.

They'd only spoken briefly over the phone. There was so much he wanted to say that he didn't know where to start. It was enough to hear her warm, caring voice agreeing to meet him and to know she hadn't changed.

SHE could have flown out to join Jon after a time. Her mother had died months after Jon left and her father, it seemed, had very many friends he relied on for companionship and comfort. When he married a widow and moved to the south coast, it was Lizzie who felt bereft.

How could she contact Jon now? She had ignored all his letters. So, she threw herself into her career and told herself she was learning to live without him.

Now, Lizzie looked at her watch again — half an hour was up.

Jon had said he was coming back on business. No doubt he'd tried to fit her into a crowded timetable of meetings and failed. She told herself it didn't matter — he would probably just have regaled her with news of an American wife and shown her snaps of children with gleaming American smiles.

Reluctantly, Lizzie was turning towards the exit when she heard shouting nearby. She turned to see a young woman bending over an elderly man.

"Dad! Dad! Oh, help!"

Lizzie didn't hesitate.

"It's all right, I'm a nurse. Try not to worry. Somebody send for an ambulance, please." Lizzie's voice was calm and authoritative as she knelt beside the man, even though her fingers were telling her there was no pulse.

"We're going to have to resuscitate your father until the ambulance arrives," she told the young woman. "This is what I want you to do . . ."

Jon swore softly as the taxi pulled over to let an ambulance pass. He could see the traffic snarled up ahead. Tapping on the window, he paid the cabbie and leapt out, deciding it would be quicker to run.

But he needn't have bothered. There was no-one standing under the clock as he hurried into the station. Glancing down, he saw a battered silk rose at his feet. He picked it up sadly, and put it in his pocket. He'd have to phone her again, try to explain.

The people on the crowded forecourt suddenly parted to let the ambulance leave, its lights flashing. And, in its wake, he saw a young woman walking away.

"Lizzie!" he shouted urgently, pushing past people to reach her. "Lizzie!"

She turned at the sound of his voice and, in two more strides, he was beside her.

STILL late — the taxi got stuck in traffic," he said ruefully. He was just as she remembered — tall and smart with brown hair flopping engagingly on to his forehead. She was aware of her crumpled skirt and ruffled hair, and she knew her face would be flushed from bending.

"Still crusading," she told him, indicating the departing ambulance. "Heart attack."

There was an awkward pause.

"I think such a pretty rescuer deserves a coffee," Jon said at last and, remembering, she couldn't resist smiling back at him.

They found a small tea-room outside the station, where Lizzie struggled to regain her composure and arrange her skirt so the ladder in her tights didn't show.

"So," she exclaimed brightly, "tell me what you've been up to. Your job . . . your family."

There was a short silence. He looked very serious and she braced herself to hear that he was married to a wonderful girl.

"My father died," he said abruptly. "Heart attack on the golf course. There was no-one there to rescue him . . . I felt very bad that I'd hardly seen him, hardly knew him . . . I was so busy with my new job."

Swaledale, Yorkshire

SHEEP and trees dot the landscape surrounding the village of Keld in Swaledale. Walkers come to enjoy the changing seasons in the Fells and trek along The Pennine Way, which wends through some of Yorkshire's prettiest scenery.

This is "James Herriot" country and it's not hard to see why the young vet fell in love with this area.

SWALEDALE: J. CAMPBELL KERR.

Lizzie didn't know what to say.

"Anyway," he said after a moment, in a more cheerful tone, "what are you doing these days?"

"Oh, I pay an outrageous rent to live in a flat in town." She matched her tone to his. "I've had three promotions and am waiting to hear about a job running the intensive care department." She smiled. "And how's your job in America?"

"The States taught me a lot," he began slowly. "It was good fun. But New York is so busy — everyone running round desperate to make money. Not much room for crusaders! The company wants to set up in Britain — so I jumped at the chance to come back."

She took a deep breath. She hadn't realised — she'd thought this was a flying visit.

"And what about all those classy New York girls?" She had to know if he'd met someone else.

"Oh, there are plenty of those! Very intelligent, go-getting career women for the most part."

Lizzie let her breath out slowly and nodded.

"Well, a woman has to look out for herself these days. I think you become more single-minded as you get older — start looking out for number one —" she broke off as he gave something between a chuckle and a cough.

"Of course, I had to respond just now when that man collapsed. That's my training . . . But I'm a lot tougher than I used to be . . ." Her voice tailed away under his warm gaze.

"That's a pity. Because all the time I was away I kept remembering a soft, pretty face and large eyes filling with tears whenever they watched 'Brief Encounter'."

Her eyes widened as he spoke.

"And every time a harsh New York accent jarred, I heard a gentle, soothing voice and a happy, infectious laugh."

"You did?" Her heart leapt.

Jon nodded.

"I think you discover the things that really matter when you're a long way from home."

Out of the corner of her eye, Lizzie saw a woman juggling a toddler, a baby and a tray of food as she tried in vain to find a table. For once, Lizzie fought down the impulse to help and met Jon's intense gaze.

"We never had enough time for each other — too many things kept getting in the way," she admitted and he pulled out the crumpled silk rosebud and laid it on the table between them.

"Perhaps we can have our time now."

She looked into his eyes and saw the years hadn't dimmed the love between them. She picked up the rose and smiled.

"I think it's going to be the best time of all." ∎

Illustration by Melvyn Warren-Smith.

The Means To An End

CAREFULLY, I ironed my husband's white shirt, smoothing the steam iron along one sleeve.

As I worked, I couldn't help marvelling at this new iron my daughter had bought me. I smiled as I remembered her comments on my old one.

"You must have had this since the war!" Joan had insisted on relegating the iron to the back of the lobby press and had produced a new model with a flourish.

"It's the Fifties now, Mother — irons have steam." She'd gone on to demonstrate and I'd certainly been impressed.

Joan had all mod cons in her home and was trying to bring me up to date, too. My daughter liked to be modern and had a job and a family.

So, I'd soon found myself organised into looking after my granddaughter after school. Hannah was a quiet soul and no trouble.

Glancing up from my ironing now, I found her watching me.

by Sylvia Store.

"Mum doesn't bother much with ironing," she said. "She says it soon gets creased again anyway."

"Oh, she's quite right," I replied cheerfully. "Old habits die hard, that's the trouble."

She nodded, raising a hand to put a strand of hair behind one ear. The red pinch-mark stood out on the soft skin of her upper arm, sharp and clear.

"Who did *that?*" I asked, pointing.

"A boy at school." She bent her head, examining the mark. "At St Herald's. I started last term."

"Yes, I know."

I remembered thinking at the time what a big upheaval it would be in her life. But her mother had said it wasn't, that Hannah had taken it all in her stride.

"And what did he do that for?"

"He's a bully," Hannah said flatly. "Just because I can run faster than him." She gave a small — a very small — sigh.

"His friends keep saying fancy being beaten by a girl and then he's really *horrible.*" She rolled her eyes.

"Poor you," I sympathised.

"Yes." She nodded. She looked as if she might manage a tear, then briskly changed her mind. "Could I have a squashed fly biscuit, Gran?"

Switching off the iron, I went into the kitchen and opened the packet of Garibaldi. She carefully took the plate from me and settled down in the armchair, taking neat, small bites out of the first biscuit.

"His name's Darren," she said, after a moment. "This boy I was telling you about."

I picked up another of Sidney's shirts and laid it out on the ironing board.

"I had trouble with a boy a bit like Darren when I was at school," I said. "I was moved up into his class. He was the marbles champion."

"Oh, marbles." Hannah looked dismissive. "They've got those in the toy shop in Frinton Street."

"They were very important when I was your age. It was our big thing, marbles. Everyone tried to collect them, to have the most. Tried to win more.

"Anyway, I beat this boy. Took quite a few of his best marbles. After that, he was *horrible* to me."

"Just like Darren."

"Mmm. He started pushing me. Jeering. Calling me names in the playground. Chasing me."

I had her full attention now; the remains of her biscuit lying forgotten on her plate.

"What happened, Gran?" She put out her free hand and touched my arm in sympathy.

"One day, one of the other children came to school with a marvellous big marble, all the colours of the rainbow shining in it." Briefly, I closed my eyes, remembering. "Hannah, I just *had* to have it . . ."

"So did the horrible boy," she said quietly.

"Yes. As much as I did. More, really. Because of his friends. They'd got on to him just like Darren's friends. Boys seem to do that, don't they? He was really unhappy."

"Served him right! You won that big marble, didn't you, Gran? I bet that showed him!"

"No," I said slowly. "I could have . . . but I didn't. I let him win it."

"Well *that* wasn't very clever of you, Gran." She looked so cross I smiled at her.

"But afterwards, he was really nice to me, Hannah. He carried my books home every day, even gave me sweets. I was rotten at maths, and he started helping me with my homework." I paused.

"You see, he'd regained his prestige with his friends — his standing, if you like. And that's just human nature. Underneath, he was a kind boy."

H UH," she began, then stopped as the back door slammed and Sidney came in from the garden. She got up and hugged him. "And what have you two been cooking up between you?" he teased, ruffling her hair.

"Oh, just talking about a boy at school," Hannah said. "He doesn't like me beating him. Gran says he should realise that men and women are equal."

"So they are," I agreed, before her grandfather could reply. "But there's ways and means to an end."

"Like getting yourself a nice big lad to sort him out for you!" Sidney chuckled.

"I can look after myself." Hannah grimaced. "I shall just wait and give him a good pinch back!"

I glanced at the clock, then slipped upstairs to a background of giggles and deep laughter from Sidney to get Hannah's coat. At the dressing-table I paused, then opened a drawer and took out my jewellery box.

Setting the top compartment to one side, I gazed down at the perfect rainbow-hued marble almost winking up at me. Gently, I picked it up and rolled it between my palms.

I'd won it, after all.

Sidney had given it to me a few days after that marbles match, when he'd asked me to be his girl. I didn't say yes straight away, of course. We were full of guile in those days.

Smiling to myself, I almost ran down the stairs. Like I'd told Hannah, there's ways and means to an end. Times change, of course. But I still reckoned I'd chosen the best route! ∎

Torren, Skye.

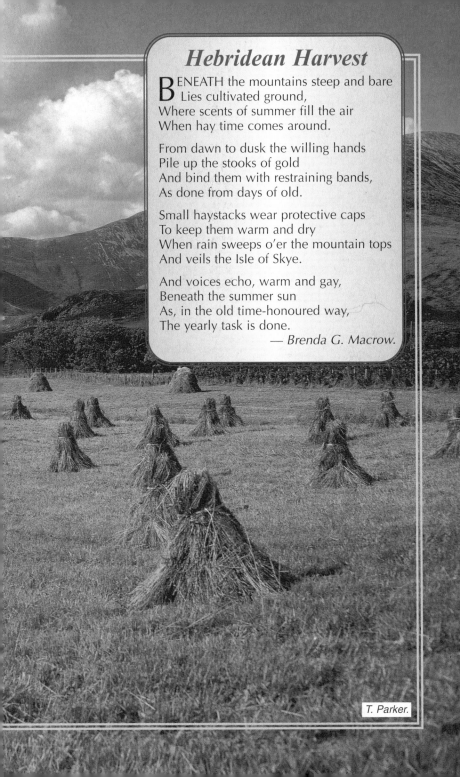

Hebridean Harvest

BENEATH the mountains steep and bare
Lies cultivated ground,
Where scents of summer fill the air
When hay time comes around.

From dawn to dusk the willing hands
Pile up the stooks of gold
And bind them with restraining bands,
As done from days of old.

Small haystacks wear protective caps
To keep them warm and dry
When rain sweeps o'er the mountain tops
And veils the Isle of Skye.

And voices echo, warm and gay,
Beneath the summer sun
As, in the old time-honoured way,
The yearly task is done.

— *Brenda G. Macrow.*

T. Parker.

L UCY! Stand still." Helen Lister knelt on the floor, speaking through a mouthful of pins. "Do you want this finished for tomorrow or not?"

"I thought it was." Lucy smoothed the palms of her hands down over the tulip-shaped wedding gown.

"So did I." Helen smiled up at her. "It's you that keeps losing weight." She pushed one of the pins into the deep satin waistband.

"It's nerves."

Helen looked up into the pretty young face; if Lucy was nervous, she didn't know what that made *her*. Her brow pleated at the thought of tomorrow; how was she going to get through the service without breaking down?

Love In Every Stitch

She dropped the remaining pins into the palm of her hand.

"You've no need to be nervous, darling. This time tomorrow you'll be married to the man you love.

"The church is booked, the reception organised down to the very last detail, and —" she paused and smoothed at the waistband again "— hopefully, you'll be wearing a gown that's a perfect fit."

Lucy nodded.

"Let's have this off, then." Helen gave a little groan as she got off her knees.

"That's how you know you're getting on a bit!" Lucy grinned.

Helen's eyebrows disappeared into her fringe.

"You know." Lucy laughed. "When you start making funny noises when you bend over or stand up."

"Thank you for that, madam!" Helen joined in her laughter as she unzipped her. "You don't know how pleased I'll be to be finished with this dress." She slipped it over a hanger.

"I hope that doesn't go for me, too." Lucy slumped on the sofa.

by Deborah Leslie.

Illustration by
Sue Heslop.

35

Helen dropped the dress over the back of the nearest chair and threw her arms around her.

"What are you thinking?" She smoothed her hair.

"I think I'm going to miss you more than I can say." Lucy pulled her down on to the sofa. "I . . . I think you're the most wonderful person I know."

"Lucy Loo!" Helen smiled as her foster daughter pulled her legs up on to the sofa, and laid her head on her shoulder.

She passed a hand over the gleaming swirl of dark hair. Lucy might be grown up now, but in many ways she was still very much the angry child they'd welcomed into their home; a temporary foster placement that had stretched to months, and then years.

She swallowed hard, even now. The anger rose within her when she remembered how the social worker had described Lucy as a "problem child".

"It's not Lucy that's got the problem, it's the adults in her life!" Helen had said firmly. "She's not bad, just incredibly sad."

Little by little, Lucy had come to trust her. Helen's arms tightened round her foster daughter. Her heart had ached for Lucy. There had been so many times when she'd unwittingly hurt her, momentarily transporting her back to darker days, causing her to question how much she was loved . . .

"Jump up, Luce!" Helen patted her affectionately. "I've got something to show you."

She leaned one hand on the top of the dresser, and pulled open one of the stiff drawers.

A small, rectangular parcel, wrapped in wedding paper, lay in her hands. She handed it to Lucy.

"But, Mum, you've already given us your wedding present." A worried look clouded her pretty face. "Michael thinks you've been more than generous already."

"This is just a little something between you and me." Helen tapped the side of her nose with one finger, and looked on as Lucy's slender fingers tore at the paper.

"A Bible." She hugged her tightly. "Thanks, Mum! It's beautiful."

"But it's not just any Bible." Helen hugged her back. "This one's special."

"It's not new." Lucy passed a hand over the cracked white leather.

"Look inside."

"Who's this?" Lucy gazed at the faded black and white photograph in the front.

"My mother and father — and that's me." She pointed at the little girl with the long pinafore dress and ringlets, adorned with a broad loop of ribbon.

Helen closed her eyes, and let the past rush up to meet her; a memory so clear and true that tears pricked behind her closed lids.

She pressed the point of her chin against her shoulder, touching the place where her mother's hand had rested as they posed. She remembered the cloying scent of the lilac hyacinths that had stood on the table behind them . . .

"Oh, Mum! You were so pretty — beautiful, even."

"Were?" she teased.

"Are!" Lucy laughed. "Inside and out. But you can't give this to me."

"Why can't I?"

"Because I'm not really family."

Helen slipped an arm around her shoulders.

"I can, and I will! My mother gave me this Bible on my wedding day. And now I'm giving it to you."

"But it's too precious! It must mean the world to you."

"Oh, Lucy, you idiot, *you* mean the world to us! This is how much I love you, how much *we* love you." She smoothed the hair back from Lucy's brow. "We're never going to stop loving you."

Lucy stared at her.

"Me neither," she said, choked, and hugged Helen again. "Dad's been wonderful, too. I love you both — so much."

"It's been our privilege." Helen kissed the top of her head. "Loving you's never been hard. You turned out to be the child we'd prayed for."

THEY both looked up as the front door opened. "That must be Dad with his outfit for tomorrow!" Helen looked over her shoulder as Trevor came into the room, a polythene-covered kilt and jacket draped over one arm.

"Hi, troops! All ready for the big day?"

Lucy leaned over the back of the sofa and caught Trevor by the hand.

"Come and sit down for a minute." She smiled shyly. "I've got something to ask you."

"Sounds intriguing." He hung his wedding outfit on the door. "Budge up, then."

He sat on her other side and reached round to cuddle her.

"OK, I'll come right to the point." Lucy took their hands in hers. "I want you both to walk me up the aisle."

"Both?" Helen and Trevor spoke at the same time.

"I want you both to be there with me." Her eyes filled with tears. "You've gone through everything with me — I can't leave you out, Mum."

Helen's vision blurred as she looked for Trevor's reaction. His eyes searched hers. She sighed. As usual, the ball was in her court.

"It's a bit unconventional, but let's do it!" She rolled her eyes heavenwards. "I must be mad, but let's do it anyway."

Help me to get through tomorrow, she thought silently. And while you're at it, grant me the stiffest upper lip in the country!

She sat alone until the small hours, making the adjustments to Lucy's

The Secret Of The Black Box

"Friend" favourite John Taylor finds a very special memento.

WE have a black tin box with a lock. But it's never actually locked. In fact, we can hardly get it shut!

Inside are all our insurance policies and guarantees for household items. There's a share certificate belonging to Anne.

Then there are a few prize certificates and a medal or two. There are also lots of receipts and little notes.

Anne must have been looking for something that afternoon just after New Year. When I came in after milking, she was sitting at the kitchen table, holding a letter.

"John, look at this. It's fifty-six years old this year."

I could detect a quiver in her voice.

With love and best wishes for your future — Grandad and me.

The note was written on a piece of paper cut out of an old exercise book. Granny had taken ages, using an old quill pen, to write, or rather print,

dress, sewing love into every stitch. Finally, satisfied, she tiptoed up to bed.

The duvet moved up and down in time with the steady rhythm of Trevor's breathing. She undressed silently, captured about a third of the duvet for herself and turned on to her side.

Pale moonlight pushed dark shadows around the room. Her tired eyes followed their progress for a while, before closing in a deep and dreamless sleep.

Morning came, and Helen felt a surge of excitement.

Trevor was still asleep. She pulled her dressing-gown on and padded downstairs.

out that loving note. It's faded slightly now, but it still bears such a wealth of meaning, love and sacrifice.

WHEN Anne and I were courting, neither of us had a telephone. So we used to ask the postmen to pass on messages.

One Christmas, I told Charlie, our postman, to ask Ian, the postman for Arncroach, to let Grandad Taylor know that Anne and I were coming for Christmas Eve supper.

We wanted to tell them we were hoping, as soon as we could, to rent a farm and get married.

As we sat milking, I told Dad we were going to visit his parents.

"That's very nice of you, boy."

Grandad had started work on a farm as a boy and ended up as a grieve. Granny had been a maid, then became a housekeeper.

Their wages had been in shillings, not pounds and, as far as we knew, they had little money. Anne and I took them a piece of rib for soup, two bacon chops, a large black pudding, some bacon and eggs.

When we arrived, they were right pleased to see us. We sat and chatted beside the fire.

"From what I hear, you two will be getting married soon."

"Where did you pick up that piece of gossip, Grandad?"

"Jim and Mabel."

I smiled. I knew Jim and Mabel well. They were family friends.

"Well, we can't get married until we get a farm to rent."

"Don't be too long. There could be a war soon and then you'll never get a farm."

A little while later, he spoke again.

"I don't suppose your mum and dad pay you a wage, laddie. How much money do you have?"

I told him. I was ashamed of the low amount.

"You'll need more than that for stock, lad. Now don't go borrowing any money. Come to us first. We haven't much, but we'll help."

We had a lovely Christmas Eve supper. Granny had made a rabbit pie, plus roast potatoes and one of Grandad's home-grown cabbages.

As we left, Granny handed Anne an envelope.

"I hope, dear, this will help you set up."

We stopped before we got to Anne's house and opened the envelope. There was a lot of money inside, plus that lovely letter.

And they wouldn't take a penny back.

"That, boy, is their life's savings," Dad said when I told him.

We were both deeply touched.

Now you'll understand why Anne and I can't throw that letter away.

The Farmer And His Wife

No-one else was going to make Lucy's wedding breakfast. The kettle began to whistle as she covered her best silver tray with a fan of lacy cloth. Humming to herself, she poured a glass of fresh orange juice and set flaky croissants on one of the best plates.

In the living-room stood Lucy's precious dress. She passed a smoothing hand over the material as she crossed the room and pulled a long-stemmed peach carnation from the arrangement in the corner.

Snapping the stalk, she set it in her favourite crystal bud vase.

Then she climbed the stairs, the dishes on the loaded tray jangling in her hands.

She pushed the bedroom door open with her shoulder.

"Morning, Lucy Loo."

Lucy was sitting up in bed, her dark hair flaring out against the pillows. Smiling, Helen set the tray on a mountain of bedclothes, and Lucy grinned.

"You're spoiling me." She picked the carnation from the sparkling vase and buried her nose in the ruffle of feathery petals.

"You deserve it. No-one deserves it more than you." She watched as Lucy bit into a croissant.

"Well, today's the day." Lucy reached for her orange juice. "I just hope everything goes according to plan."

"What could go wrong?" Helen sat down on the bed and smiled at her.

"The only thing that you've got to worry about is how I'm going to get through the service without bursting into tears."

"Tears and weddings go together!" Lucy swept a moistened finger around the plate, collecting every stray crumb. "Anyway, you're always so strong."

"Not when it comes to you. You're my one big weakness."

THE black hands of the old grandfather clock in the hall seemed to spin as the whirlwind of preparations went on. Bouquets, Lucy's garland, and the basket of flowers arrived and the pair of anxious flower girls.

Helen smiled at them as they stood shivering with excitement. Then she slipped the hooped skirts over their tiny, outstretched arms.

"You know, I think I'll pop over to the church and check that everything's as it should be." She smiled across at Lucy. "I just want to have a look at the posies on the end of the pews, and maybe have a word with the new organist . . ."

Trevor looked up from polishing his brogues.

"Leave well alone, woman! Everything will be just fine."

Helen nodded, unconvinced. She went upstairs and dressed herself carefully. Her hands shook as she arranged her hair in front of the mirror.

Squirting perfume behind her ears, she made a face at her reflection; she'd never been a dressing-up kind of girl.

"Mum! It's here." Lucy's voice screamed up the stairs, and she lifted the edge of the net curtain.

The carriage was turning into the end of the drive, drawn by a fine-looking pair of horses, a top-hatted driver holding the reins.

"I can't believe I'm actually going to the church in that." Lucy bounded up to meet her, a picture in the dress that had taken so long to make.

Helen joined her at the small-paned window, peering down at the horses coming to rest in front of the house, their shiny hindquarters bathed in dappled sunlight.

"Only the best will do for our only daughter." She squeezed Lucy's shoulder.

"I think I'm going to cry." Lucy's bottom lip trembled under the strain.

"Don't you dare!" Helen pointed towards the door. "We've got a wedding to go to."

Helen took a deep breath as the horses clip-clopped to a halt outside the small church that she loved so much.

Trevor got down first, his kilt swinging. He lifted the flower girls from their seats, and they squealed with delight as he spun them round.

"I could do with your help," Helen said, as the carriage swayed to her movements. His hand was strong, reassuring.

Lucy stood up in the carriage smiling.

"My skirt's not wide enough, Dad, you'll have to lift me!" Her earrings danced as she laughed.

Helen stood with her arms around the little girls' shoulders as Trevor scooped their daughter up in his arms.

"All ready, Lucy?" The vicar arrived, beaming. "I'll just let Michael know you decided to turn up!"

"This is it then." Lucy turned towards her as they went into the church. Helen felt hot tears rush to her eyes. She glowed with pride and happiness when Lucy made twin loops with her arms. The wedding march began to play.

Slowly, they made their way up the aisle on either side of Lucy. She nodded at the small gathering of family and friends, enjoying their varied reactions to this rather unusual sight.

Her knees shook as they approached the end of the aisle and delivered Lucy to her beloved Michael.

She stood with Trevor, listening to the time-honoured words, remembering . . .

Remembering how they'd stood here, 30 years ago this year, while dear old Mr Adams had said those same words to them . . . How Trevor's hand had trembled, just as Michael's was doing now, as he'd slipped the ring on her finger . . .

Remembering the children's services, just after they'd married, and how heavy their hearts had been, knowing they'd never have a child of their own to bring them Easter daffodils . . .

Remembering the joy of bringing Lucy here that first Christmas, the glow of the candles reflecting in her shining eyes . . .

Then the service was over, the register signed, and Michael and Lucy were about to set back off down the aisle as man and wife.

"Mum!" She was suddenly enfolded in Lucy's arms. "Carry my flowers back for me, please. I've got something else to take with me . . ."

And Helen followed them through the church, watching her daughter holding hands with her husband, while in the other hand she clutched her mother's Bible. ■

Led A Merry Dance

THERE were never enough men to go around in the Eckersleigh Sequence Dance Club. The club met three afternoons a week in the local church hall, from two until four-thirty, with tea and biscuits at half-time.

Harold and Daphne organised everything; he put on the music and his wife chose the dances. Together, they demonstrated any dances that were new or unfamiliar.

All the men, married as well as single, were expected to dance now and again with any lady who

by Marion Scales.

had no regular partner. Usually this caused no problem; the ladies liked to have a gossip together, so they didn't mind sitting out a dance or two.

Then a new member arrived to join the club and everything seemed to change.

She turned up during teatime and all eyes were riveted on her as she filled in her membership form at Harold and Daphne's table.

"Crikey," Joan exclaimed, nudging her friend, "what's she

come as? The Princess Royal?"

"Ooh, that's a lovely dress, though," Eileen said. "I love cerise, especially with blonde hair. And she's certainly got the figure for it."

"She must have a good girdle on to get her waist that small," Margaret mumbled through a custard cream.

"And a good hairdresser. I can't believe that's her natural colour."

"It looks natural to me," Larry said. "I think she looks smashing."

The three women glared at

him so he quickly picked up his cup of tea and gulped at it awkwardly.

Joan pointed to the newcomer's feet.

"She can't be a very good dancer. She's not wearing silver shoes."

"Maybe she's got suede soles — like me," Larry put in.

Eileen groaned. Larry was always going on about his suede soles. After every few dances, he would take out his wire brush and

42

Illustration by Atsuko Fujii.

give them a quick going over.

"Shush," she warned. "They're coming over."

Harold and Daphne introduced the new club member as Rosina. Close up, she was even more attractive and Larry stood up to offer his chair. Then he dashed off to fetch her a cup of tea.

"Rosina's recently moved here," Daphne told them. "She was a ballerina in her younger

43

days. But she enjoys other sorts of dancing, too."

"That must be where you got your marvellous figure," Margaret said enviously, tucking into a chocolate digestive.

"I do try to keep fit," Rosina replied. "That's why I took up sequence dancing. I think it helps to keep my mind active, too. Learning and remembering all the new dances can be quite a challenge."

Larry returned with Rosina's tea just as Daphne announced a Melody Fox-trot. He held a hand out to her.

"Shall we?"

Rosina took his hand and stepped gracefully on to the dance floor.

Margaret and Joan watched in amazement. Margaret couldn't help feeling a little annoyed — Larry usually danced the Melody Fox-trot with her. But she had to admit Larry and Rosina danced beautifully together, never missing a beat.

The first song finished and another man cut in on Larry to partner Rosina for the second dance. Larry went back to his table and asked Margaret up.

"She's a wonderful dancer," he told her tactlessly. "She glides across the floor as if she's on ice-skates."

Harold usually played the same dance tune twice, to give everyone a turn. So, at the end of the two dances, everyone left the floor for a minute or two while he searched for the next record.

Daphne announced the next dance would be a Square Tango — always very popular. Eight men immediately clustered round Rosina.

"Like bees around a honey-pot," Joan grumbled.

AS the weeks went by, the woman gradually formed a grudging respect for Rosina, though they still kept her at a distance. Although she was always first on the floor, she made sure she never danced with the same man more than once or twice each session, and she occasionally sat dances out and would chat with Daphne.

One afternoon during tea, Daphne made an announcement.

"Would everyone who wants to come on the sequence dance weekend at Chandlers' Holiday Centre please put their names on the sheet Harold's bringing round? There'll be lots of competitions and I'd like plenty of time for rehearsals."

A buzz of excitement went through the hall. Everyone loved their twice-yearly dancing trips. This was the first time they'd chosen to go to Chandlers', but they'd had good reports about it from other clubs.

"Are you going to come, Rosina?" Larry sounded hopeful.

"I wouldn't miss it for the world." She smiled. "Perhaps we could enter one of the competitions together."

Larry was delighted, certain he'd win with Rosina as his partner.

On the next club day, Margaret, Eileen and Joan arrived together as usual. They were about ten minutes early and were surprised to find

Rosina and a large group of men already in the hall. Rosina was talking, but they couldn't hear what she was saying. They did hear the roar of laughter that went up from the men, though.

"I wonder what she's up to," Joan said suspiciously.

The women sidled closer, but all they heard was Rosina telling a joke.

Margaret took Larry's arm.

"What's going on?"

"Nothing much." He shrugged. "Rosina was just telling us a few stories from her ballet-dancing days."

"How come all you men are here so early? And how come she is, too?"

Larry shrugged.

"Dunno. Must be a lucky coincidence."

Margaret wasn't convinced and watched Rosina all afternoon. Her nosiness paid off when she saw Rosina handing Larry a note.

She buttonholed him by the tea urn.

"What was that — a love letter?" she said, trying to sound lighthearted.

Larry stared at her, astonished.

"If you've got something to say, Margaret, then I wish you'd come right out with it."

"All right then." She swallowed hard. "I don't like the way Rosina's always sniffing round you. She seems to be after all the men in the club, married or not."

"Why, are you jealous then?" The idea rather pleased him.

"Don't be stupid," Margaret retorted, a bit too quickly. "I just don't like to see you making a fool of yourself, that's all."

Larry kissed her cheek affectionately — they'd been friends for a long time.

"Don't worry about me. I'm old enough to know what I'm doing."

He poured out two cups of tea, collected a plate of biscuits and invited Margaret to sit with him.

ON the last Friday in September the club members set off bright and early for their dancing weekend. There were forty-two of them altogether — seventeen men and twenty-five women.

"Did you see how many cases Rosina brought?" Eileen whispered as they sat at the back of the bus. "I counted at least six."

"Maybe she's decided to stay for a month. Give her more of a chance to catch a man," Margaret joked.

"I don't think she wants one man." Eileen giggled. "She wants a string of them, like racehorses."

"More like a herd of old goats, if you ask me."

Daphne made her way down the coach, handing out copies of the itinerary and chalet numbers. The chalets were for two, so all the single

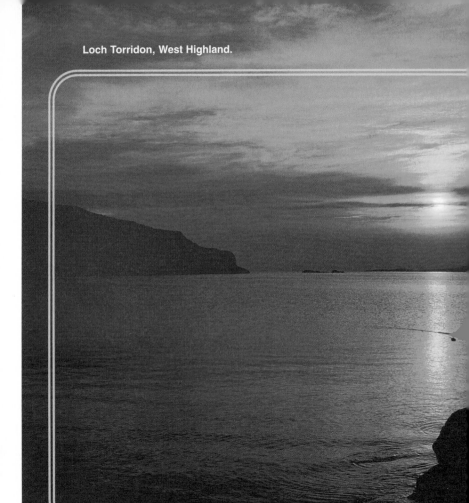

Loch Torridon, West Highland.

members would be sharing. Eileen and Margaret were to be next door to Rosina. Eileen stopped Daphne as she made her way back up the coach.

"How come her ladyship's got a chalet all to herself?"

"Because there are twenty-five women and I couldn't very well put her in with the odd man, could I?"

"But you never asked me if I wanted it," Eileen grumbled.

"That's because you'd already said you wanted to share with Margaret," Daphne replied patiently. "Anyway, Rosina especially asked to be on her own, if possible."

"Oh?" Eileen raised her eyebrows.

Fisherman

THE angler stands at sunset
   Where silent shadows steal,
Nothing disturbs the stillness
But the whirr of his spinning reel.

Patiently, ever hopeful,
He casts in the changing light,
Watching the golden ripples,
Hoping the fish will bite.

Yet, there is more to fishing
Than he'd perhaps declare,
This is a time of leisure,
An escape from daily care.

Here he's alone with nature,
Part of an ancient scheme —
Man, the eternal hunter,
Lost in a timeless dream.

And if the fish elude him,
Still he'll find release,
Breathing the ocean's fragrance,
Sharing the evening's peace.
                    — *Brenda G. Macrow.*

T. Parker.

Everyone was thoroughly enjoying the weekend. The food was excellent and the ballroom perfect, with a large, well-chalked floor.

On Friday evening there had been a dinner dance with a ten-piece band. It had been a chance for the various clubs to relax and socialise, to renew friendships made on previous occasions.

Then, on Saturday afternoon, they all went along to a tea dance and, in the evening, the serious competitions began. The Eckersleigh Club had entered only three categories: Best Group Tango, Most Elegant Couple and Best Organisers.

Daphne had entered Rosina and Larry in the Most Elegant Couple contest. They had to dance a waltz while the judges strolled around, taking notes.

Margaret and Eileen watched anxiously as the judges walked past Rosina and Larry, seemingly without a glance. Despite their reservations about Rosina, they still wanted her and Larry to win.

Finally, the judges went into a huddle. Seconds later, they handed their decision to the MC, who was to announce the winners. He took his time opening the envelope in order to build up the tension.

"And the winners are —" he paused while the drummer did a resounding roll on the snare "— Eckersleigh!"

A big roar of approval went up from the crowd as Larry and Rosina collected their cup.

A SPECIAL dinner was laid on for Sunday and the evening was to be a party night. The main competition was a Novelty Dance Contest.

Eileen and Margaret went into the ballroom early as they wanted to be sure of getting good seats. They sat down by some ladies they'd made friends with the previous evening.

"Are you going in for the competition tonight?" they asked.

"No. Our club never bothers with the silly ones. We can't seem to agree on anything funny enough," Eileen told them. "How about you?"

"It's supposed to be a surprise, but it won't hurt to tell you. Our five fattest ladies are doing a 'Roly Polys' tap dance."

"Pity we didn't think of that, Margaret." Eileen giggled. "You could have been the star."

Margaret leaned over to give her friend a playful slap, but managed to knock the table, spilling coffee all over her dress.

"I'll have to go and change," she said, mortified, dashing off to her chalet.

As she rounded the corner of her row, she noticed two men going into one of the chalets near hers. When she got closer, she realised it was Rosina's!

While she was changing, Margaret distinctly heard men's voices and laughter. When she realised one of the voices sounded like Larry's, she decided to go and investigate.

When she knocked briskly on Rosina's door, she heard a lot of rustling noises and muffled voices. Then the door opened a crack and Rosina peered out.

"Oh, it's you, Margaret. Is something wrong?"

"No, I, er," she stammered, thinking furiously. "I wondered if you'd got an iron I could borrow for a minute, please?"

"No problem. I'll just get it for you." Rosina shut the door while she went to get the iron.

Margaret peeped in the window but the curtains were shut tight. She jumped back quickly as the door opened.

Rosina thrust the iron through the gap.

"Here you are, Margaret. You can let me have it back in the morning."

As soon as Margaret had taken it, the door closed again. She popped the iron into her own chalet and then walked as fast as she could back to the ballroom, impatient to tell her friends what had happened.

Eileen and Joan were agog with excitement when Margaret related the story to them.

"We were beginning to wonder where the men had gone," Eileen admitted. "If they don't get here by the time the dancing starts after the competition, I think we ought to go to fetch them."

JUST then, the MC announced the first of the Novelty Dance entries, which diverted the women's attention to the dance floor.

Five well-rounded, elderly ladies tap danced their way through a routine, raising plenty of laughs and a good round of applause. More entries followed.

Suddenly, Rosina appeared from nowhere and sat down next to Margaret. She was slightly out of breath. Margaret gave her a strange look, but before she could say anything, the lights over the dance floor were dimmed and the MC announced the final entrants.

"Please welcome the Eckersleigh Sequence Dance Club with their routine entitled, 'Ballerina Basketball'."

The lights came on and then men dressed in pink tutus, purple and green striped tights, and pink ballet shoes, tiptoed on to the dance floor. To music from Swan Lake, they performed a graceful, balletic basketball game, using a ball covered in purple fur-fabric. The whole audience rocked with laughter.

"That's Larry." Margaret pointed him out in amazement. "And there's Harold." She turned to Rosina.

"So that's what's been going on!"

"We decided to keep it a secret," Rosina admitted. "They wanted to surprise you all. Everyone has worked really hard, practising their routine. I've been teaching them at my house."

Margaret sighed in relief.

"I'm sorry," she said at last. "We all seem to have jumped to the wrong conclusion."

Rosina accepted her apology and smiled wryly.

"You can stop worrying that I'm trying to beguile all the men at the club now."

They all nodded.

"Anyway, from next week, I'll have a regular partner — my husband. He's just retired. But I don't think we'll be winning competitions — he has two left feet!"

And everyone laughed. ∎

by Christine Shinwell.

PENNY came in from shopping, gasping for a cup of tea. She glanced at her watch. Yes, there was just time before she had to prepare a meal. Melanie was spending the afternoon with her friends from school, and tonight they were all going to the sixth-form disco.

She'll need a snack before she goes, though, Penny thought, filling the kettle.

As she put her purchases away, she realised sadly that it wouldn't be long before she'd be shopping for just one . . . eating alone and living alone.

How dull life would seem without her bubbly daughter.

If only Melanie hadn't given her such a shock! Penny had known she longed to travel, but she hadn't thought she'd be setting off as soon as she left school in the summer.

And Australia, of all places. It was so far away!

"It's only for a year, Mum," Melanie had said, seeing how upset Penny was when she'd told her.

"I'm not emigrating there. I just feel this is the best time to do it, while I've got the chance."

Time To Let Go

50

Only a year! Penny's heart sank. It would seem a very long year to her. Besides, Melanie might meet someone in Australia and never come back.

"Have you thought this through?" she'd asked, hoping she could talk her out of it.

"A young woman on her own. I'd be worried about you. You could get a good job here when you've done your A-levels — and you've a nice home, too!"

"Oh, Mum. Plenty of girls travel. And there's more to life than staying at home and getting a good job!"

"But where will you live?" Penny started to feel really alarmed. It was obvious Melanie had made up her mind.

"And what about paying for it all? Australia isn't just round the corner."

"I've got some money saved and I'll get a summer job after the exams," Melanie had replied with determination.

"As long as I've got enough for the airfare and for digs when I arrive, I'll manage. I'll be able to pick up work when I get there."

"It sounds as though you've got it all sussed out." Penny had sounded sharper than she'd intended.

She'd struggled so hard to bring Melanie up on her own after Tom had died. They were best friends, as well as mother and daughter.

51

She'd miss her so much.

"*Please*, Mum, don't be like this," Melanie had appealed to her, her face concerned and anxious.

"I simply want to see a bit of the world before I settle down. I've got to lead my own life now I'm grown up."

The truth of her words had struck Penny.

"Yes, I can see that," she'd snapped, annoyed with herself for feeling tearful. "I just hadn't expected you to walk out of *my* life so quickly, that's all."

That was a month ago. Since then they'd had another argument and their normally delightful relationship was strained.

The worst of it was, Penny could see her daughter's point of view. She even envied her the greater opportunities young women had these days. But that did nothing to ease the sense of impending loss she felt.

For so many years, Melanie had been the centre of her life. She'd had to juggle a full-time job with being both mother and father to her child. There hadn't been time for much socialising, other than school events.

With Melanie gone, there would be a huge void in her life, not to mention the worry of knowing her daughter was on her own in a foreign country.

As the days went by, Penny found the atmosphere between them almost as upsetting as the prospect of Melanie's trip itself.

Somehow I've got to come to terms with her wishes and make things right between us, she decided, getting out a cup and saucer. I can't bear the thought of our spending her last months at home at loggerheads.

She spooned some tea into the pot and looked at the old tea caddy. It had stood on that dresser shelf for as long as she could remember.

Her parents had bequeathed her both the dresser and the caddy when they'd died. The items were a part of her childhood.

She smiled as she remembered how her father had loved his cups of tea.

As she walked with her own cup into the sitting-room, it was as if she were walking back down the years . . .

STORY! Story!"

As a little girl, Penny would often watch her parents going through the familiar ritual of making tea, and she'd bounce up and down with excitement.

Her father would smile, his eyes sparkling, then he'd wink to tell her what was coming. He didn't *always* sit her on his knee and tell her a story, of course. But he often did, and she loved it.

The stories that came out of her daddy's head! There was no-one like him in all the world . . . and he seemed to have seen most of it!

"When I was a young man, I took a trip through all sorts of countries," he told her. "Including China, where they grow tea. Those are Chinese people on the caddy."

The caddy was a favourite with her mother, and Penny adored it, too.

It was black with a gold and red border top and bottom, and on the sides were fascinating pictures of strange-looking people in funny clothes, and flowers she'd never seen in her mummy and daddy's garden. The lid was pretty, too, with another colourful picture, and inside was the tea.

How dark it looked and what an odd smell it had. Perhaps it helped Daddy tell such good stories!

It was wonderful, sitting there on his knee, with her mother opposite them. His arm would be around her and she'd cuddle up close, listening to the deep rumble of his voice. She liked the way his eyes had little lines round them that looked to her like sunshine when he smiled.

"Tell me about the people in China, Daddy," she'd often say. "And how you got the fan."

The ladies on the side of the tea caddy had fans, and her daddy had brought one back for her mother. Mummy looked lovely with her fan.

"Well, one day . . . "

It didn't matter that the story was a different one each time. She wished she could have her hair done like the ladies in the picture on the side of the tea caddy.

As she got older, her father's stories became less fanciful.

"I really did visit a lot of countries," he told her. She'd be sitting next to him on the settee now, and drinking her own cup of tea.

"I left home when I was just seventeen, and I was intent on seeing the world. My mum said I had the wanderlust!"

He told her about all the places he'd been and how, when he'd returned home, he'd met her mother and fallen in love.

It all seemed so romantic, and those tea-time chats held a cherished place in her heart.

As she grew older still, she'd sometimes make the tea, taking the caddy carefully down from the dresser and still loving its oriental decoration.

She'd always felt there was something mysterious about it, as though it held a secret.

She felt very close to her father, too, and learned a lot about him from what he told her.

"When I got to Africa . . ." he'd say. Or, "I remember in India . . ."

Penny hadn't inherited his longing to travel, but it was obvious he'd loved his globe-trotting, for he frequently talked about it.

She carried on reminiscing, fond thoughts she'd almost forgotten coming to mind.

She could remember so many things her father had told her, as she sat there, all these years later, sipping her tea.

ISLAY and Jura may be close neighbours, but they are worlds apart in character and atmosphere. The bays and beaches of Islay contrast starkly with Jura's imposing mountains. These lovely isles do have something in common, however — whisky!

Peat is still cut on the mosslands on Islay. Its wonderful fragrance permeates the air at every turn, and it is the peat which gives Islay whiskies their unique flavour.

Steeped in history, Islay's malts are testament to a small community's way of life. Some have been produced for over 200 years, reflecting the dedication and spirit of the islanders.

The same basic whisky-making process is used by most of the distilleries on the island, but the character of each of the malts is surprisingly different. Bowmore Distillery, however, is the only one on the island to malt its own barley. It's fascinating to watch (and equally nice to smell!) the process on their special tours.

Each Islay whisky captures some essence of the place — from the fresh sea breezes to the amber sunsets, and from the rich texture of the soil to the warm welcome which visitors receive.

I was greeted by a very friendly welcome party on my last visit to

A Taste Of

Bowmore, Islay's capital.

PENNY got up and went back into the kitchen. Melanie would be home soon and she wanted time to talk to her. She was just finishing preparing their snack when she heard the front door open and close. A moment later Melanie came into the kitchen.

"Hi, Mum." She smiled uncertainly. "That smells good."

"Hello, love. It's almost ready." Penny spoke cheerfully, trying as usual to hide the awkwardness between them.

Five minutes later they were sitting down having their meal.

"Mum," Melanie began, "about Australia. I'm sorry I upset you —"

"No, it was my fault," Penny cut in. "I'm sorry, too. I've been remembering what my father once told me. About how upset his mother was when he decided he wanted to leave home and travel.

"They had the most awful row before he left, and neither of them made the effort to patch things up. He told me how, when he eventually returned home, his mother was in tears — not because he'd gone, but because she hadn't given him her blessing.

slay and Jura

Jura. As I drove off the ferry at Feolin, a couple of collie dogs, obviously owned by a farmer there, met me with their tails a-wagging.

In fact, Jura is a haven for all sorts of wildlife. The name, Jura, means deer island, and this is

Bowmore Distillery.

Peat cutting.

certainly apt since it is home to over 6000 red deer.

The island's lochs and burns are excellent for a peaceful spot of trout fishing or, alternatively, there are countless pretty sites at which to stop for a picnic.

A visit to Jura wouldn't be complete without a trip to the island's only distillery, which is in Craighouse. You have to make an appointment to visit, but it's well worth the effort.

"He'd gone anyway, so all the heartache was in vain. She'd spent the whole time regretting the resentment between them and dreading he might not come back."

She smiled at Melanie.

"*And* my father admitted he'd felt so guilty it had spoiled his 'little adventure', as he called it, to some extent." Penny's voice grew soft.

"I don't want that for you, love. If you're going, I'd rather you go happily and enjoy yourself. I think I know where you got your wanderlust from!"

"Oh, Mum, I'm so glad you understand . . ."

Penny quietly got up and went to the dresser. She reached for the old tea caddy and took it back to the table.

It hadn't contained tea for years now, but instead it held something rather special. She opened it and tipped out the contents.

"As you know, I've saved odd bits of money in here over the years and it had mounted up. Some of it's in the bank for safekeeping. I never said, but I wanted to be able to give it to you as a special gift at a special time.

"I think that time's arrived. I hope it will help you get to Australia."

"Oh, Mum . . ." Melanie got up and gave her mother a big hug.

"I've been so worried I almost decided not to go. This is wonderful of you. But are you sure?"

Penny looked at Melanie's anxious face and longed to say, *No, please stay.*

But she saw the yearning there, too, and knew she'd never forgive herself for spoiling her daughter's dreams.

She'd survive somehow. And their love would be the stronger for it.

"Yes, I'm sure," she said softly. "Besides, I remembered something else my father told me . . . how his going encouraged his mother to make a new life for herself.

"When he got home, she admitted it had done her good, because she'd made new friends and done things she wouldn't have done otherwise. And *she* had a husband!"

Melanie smiled.

"I didn't like to say anything, but I've felt for ages that's what you need to do. I think it would make you happier, Mum. I've been thinking of going to Australia for a while, but I didn't know how to break it to you. When I come back, you'll have lots of new things to tell me!"

"I hope so!" Penny squeezed her hand.

"Before you said anything, I was going to tell you something which I hope will help stop you worrying so much while I'm away," Melanie added.

"This afternoon, two of my friends told me they've decided they'd like to come with me, and one of them has an uncle down under who's offered to put us up until we get on our feet. How's that?"

Penny felt a surge of relief.

"Oh, darling, that's great. It will help so much to know you're not alone — and not sleeping under the stars!"

Penny grinned as she gathered up the money and popped it back in the caddy.

"I've always loved that caddy," Melanie said. "Just as much as you and Grandma did."

Penny turned it gently in her hands.

"I always felt it held a secret," she murmured. "Now I know what it was. It's taught me the true meaning of love."

They smiled at each other, and Penny felt the bond between them grow stronger than ever. Whatever happened, she knew now it would always be there.

"Right," she said briskly, putting the caddy back on its shelf, "off you go and get ready, or you'll be late for the disco!"

"Thanks, Mum. You're the best," Melanie said as she went, smiling, out of the room.

And those are the best words I could have wished to hear, thought Penny, her heart lifting as she cleared the table. ∎

Through Thick and Thin

"TWENTY years married today, Teddy. How about that?" I said as I made the bed.

I'd been talking to my Teddy since the age of three and had no intention of stopping now. I put him in his customary place and went downstairs.

"Sorry I won't be here, Fay," my husband, Larry, had said a few days ago. "But this business trip's unavoidable. I'll be home by lunch-time, though, and we'll have the rest of the day to celebrate our anniversary. We can go to our favourite restaurant."

He'd smiled and given me a great big hug to compensate for the one I'd miss on our special day.

In fact, his absence had suited me fine. I'd decided on two new varieties of rhododendron as an anniversary present for him, and it meant I could pop along to the garden centre before he got back and choose the best ones on the day. I knew he'd love them.

I'd also wanted to get him something a little more personal, but hadn't had any wondrous flashes of inspiration. It would have to be that gardening book he was after. I could get that at the same time.

I made some toast and coffee, then put on a CD to fill the silence. Our youngest child, Theo, had recently joined the Army, and I couldn't help missing him. Come to that, I missed all three of them.

by Virginia Lake.

57

Our eldest, Amy, was married, and Hayley had moved in with her boyfriend a few months back. The house seemed terribly quiet, and I was still battling with the empty-nest syndrome. I felt as if I wasn't needed any more.

"You need a new interest other than just work," Larry had said.

But it wasn't that easy! My family had taken up most of my time for many years, and I was finding it hard to let go. I was the maternal type, but unfortunately no-one needed mothering now!

I'd just finished my breakfast when the post came. There was a pile of anniversary cards, including a lovely one from Larry and three super ones from the children. Then the doorbell rang.

Who else could be calling this early, I asked myself as I went to open the door.

"Morning, ma'am! Sign here, please." It was a courier, beaming at me from behind a large, intriguing-looking box.

I took the paper and signed.

"Enjoy!" the cheerful fellow said as he put the box in my hands and went off whistling down the path.

I closed the door with my shoulder and carried the box into the kitchen.

With a thrill of excitement, I grabbed a knife and slit the packing tape, peering inside like a curious child.

Inside was another, prettier box, gift-wrapped. I ignored the little card and opened it.

I caught my breath as I reached inside and drew out a lovely Teddy bear. He had beady eyes, a saucy face and a flamboyant bow tied round his neck.

I opened the card with a lump in my throat, I already knew who it was from.

Happy Anniversary and all my love. From Larry.

I sat down, the bear on my lap. The significance of the gift brought tears to my eyes.

On our wedding day, knowing how much I adored Teddy bears, Larry had lightheartedly presented me with one to mark the start of our married life together . . .

O H, darling, it's gorgeous!" I laughingly hugged the little Teddy bear to me and kissed my handsome new husband. "Glad you like it, honey," he said in his American drawl. Larry was a G.I. and we'd met while I was studying for a year in Germany.

Amusingly, his middle name was Theodore, after President Roosevelt, who'd also given his name to Teddy bears.

He'd left the army as soon as he could after we were married, and we'd moved to this country, bears and all. I had three — one from childhood, one I'd won in a raffle and now Wedding Bells Teddy, as we jokingly called him.

He was a lovely Teddy, not very big but with lovely soft red pads on his feet. He had pride of place beside my dressing-table.

"He looks smarter than I do," Larry would joke as Teddy got a regular brush and spruce up.

When the children were born, they loved him as much as I did.

"I'm afraid to say Wedding Bells Teddy is no longer my own!" I told Larry.

First Amy took a fancy to him, then when Hayley arrived he was soon included in all sorts of activities. He took up residence in the girls' bedrooms, and had to divide his sleeping hours between each of their beds to avoid arguments.

"We'll get another Teddy bear," Larry told his daughters — but the new arrival didn't compare. "Weddy", as he was nicknamed, was their favourite.

When baby Theo joined the family, the first thing he saw when he got home was Weddy being waved at him. It came as no surprise that he grew as fond of the bear as the girls were.

Larry and I had our ups and downs like any other couple, but on the whole we were a happy and contented family. We had a comfortable home, good jobs and three fantastic kids.

Throughout their childhood, the little Teddy was an adaptable and much-loved companion.

"He's sitting with *me*," Amy, as eldest, would announce when we went on holidays.

"And me!" the other two would shout in quick succession.

Weddy took everything in his stride. He survived being lugged round the beach and fed sand-sprinkled sandwiches. He even got his toes wet!

"That bear of mine will be ruined by the time I get him back," I moaned to Larry with a smile on my face.

"Never mind, honey. When we celebrate our silver wedding, I'll buy you another."

He kissed me, and I decided I had the most marvellous husband in the world, and the happiest family.

L ITTLE did I know that not long afterwards Larry was to be made redundant, and he got so depressed our marriage came under real strain.

We'd argue endlessly, something we'd never done before. I had to be so careful what I said to him, and having three boisterous children around didn't help.

However, we stuck together and struggled through. Eventually he got another job which he enjoyed more than his original one.

"Sorry for behaving like a bear with a sore head," he said ruefully.

"It's made me appreciate the good times we'd had," I told him, as I put

Quirang, Skye

THIS strange, green landscape forms the northern end of Skye's Trotternish Ridge. Stretching for approximately 15 miles, Trotternish boasts eerie pinnacles and rock towers, cliffs and crags.

Take the winding road from the crofting township of Staffin towards Uig, where ferries cross to the Outer Hebrides, for the best views of Quirang. Or, better still, join the sheep on the narrow pathway and discover breathtaking views of the Outer Isles, Torridon and Knoydart.

QUIRANG, SKYE: J. CAMPBELL KERR.

my arms around him. "And I'm looking forward to the good ones of the future . . ."

The years went by and Wedding Bells Teddy got tattier and more loved as each one passed. By the time the kids reached their teens, Theo was growing out of him, but I knew the old bear still stirred up cherished memories.

"He's sitting in the girls' bedroom, surrounded by pin-ups, frilly underwear and nail polish," I said to Larry. "Where did you get such a cool bear?"

"He was meant for a real cool girl." He grinned, sweeping me into his arms and kissing me as passionately as the day we were married.

Gradually though, I started resenting the amount of time Larry had to spend away on business.

"Three teenagers is a lot to handle on my own." I flared up one evening. My mother was ill, and there was a lot of stress at work. I was finding it difficult to cope on my own.

"Amy's impossible and Hayley's not bothering to work for her GCSEs the way she should. Theo needs a man around — not an absent father!"

"Well, what am I supposed to do? Give up my job? Loads of people have to work long hours these days and go where they're told to. I don't like being away any more than you!"

The answer to our problem came in the form of a move to another office. Larry didn't have to travel so much any more, and we settled back into our comfortable routine. The girls got over their rebellious phase, while Theo matured into a fine sportsman and a son to be proud of.

Weddy still had his uses, however.

First he was used as a subject at Amy's art class, then Hayley commandeered him as an "extra" in her school play!

I stood up and went to the girls' old bedroom. He was still there and I picked him up. I looked at his scruffy ears and patchy fur, his face grubby but still smiling and his pads which had turned a dirty shade of red.

He might be older and more worn than my new bear but he was no less precious.

Larry and I were the same in a way . . . we'd been through some good times and some bad, but we'd come through closer and meaning more to each other than ever.

For a time I'd given my Teddy to my kids, just as I'd also given them my energy and devotion — but now it was time to go back to the way we were. "Just we three", as Larry used to joke before the children were born.

"You're going to get your first wash and brush up in years," I told Weddy. "Now we've both done our bit for the kids, you can come back to our bedroom, where you belong."

Almost hearing the wedding bells as they'd peeled out with joy on my wedding day, I took him to the kitchen and gave him a good spruce up. It was like giving myself a refresher, too! I felt delightfully silly and childish as I dried him off with my hairdryer.

Then I popped him back next to my dressing-table. It was as if he'd never been gone.

Tomorrow I'd look into that course I'd fancied doing for years — and maybe I'd even try a bit of pottery, I promised myself. Suddenly the future looked tempting and exciting.

I slipped on my jacket and was about to go to the garden centre when the phone rang. How typical!

"Hello?"

I smiled as I heard Amy's voice wishing us a happy anniversary.

OH, honey, they're lovely!" Larry said later on, when he saw his rhododendrons. He'd got home in good time and given me a beautiful necklace.

"I love my new Teddy bear as well!" I told him.

While Larry was changing, he was amused to see Weddy back in our bedroom.

"We're starting a new phase in our lives, aren't we, Weddy?" I said with a grin. "It's called life after kids!"

We went to a local restaurant for lunch and had a delicious meal. Over coffee I took out the small package I'd bought on the way back from the garden centre.

"Happy anniversary, darling," I said with a loving smile as I passed it across to Larry.

He looked pleasantly surprised then picked it up and unwrapped it. He came to the long plush gift box inside and carefully opened it.

Joy illuminated his face.

"A miniature grandmother clock! Oh, Fay . . ."

"Well, you've always been mad about clocks, haven't you? Almost as bad as me and my Teddy bears! I bought you a tiny grandfather clock when we got married, so I decided a matching pair would be appropriate now . . . especially as we're about to become grandparents."

"*Grand*parents?"

I laughed.

"Amy phoned this morning. She's expecting! She's known for a few days, but thought it would make a rather special anniversary present."

"I'll say!"

"Not only was it marvellous news, but it also solved my dilemma of what else to buy you. I think the little grandmother clock will go well with the grandfather, don't you?"

He returned my sparkling smile.

"Perfectly. And you'll make as good a grandma as you always have a wife and mother." He leaned across the table and kissed me. ∎

Run, Rabbit, Run!

P OLLY stopped in her tracks, the tune she'd been humming dying
on her lips.

"Oh, no!"

The little door to the rabbit hutch was ajar.

She rushed across the lawn — perhaps she wouldn't be too late to stop
Goldie doing a runner . . . but the hutch was empty and Polly's heart sank.
She mustn't have shot the bolt home properly . . .

"You will look after Goldie, won't you?" Lucy had asked as Polly had
helped her pack for a guide camping trip.

"Don't forget to feed Goldie," Lucy had said as Polly had driven her to
meet the coach.

"You will give Goldie a cuddle now and then, won't you?" Lucy had
asked as she'd boarded the coach.

Even as the coach had pulled away, Lucy was on her feet and shouting
out of the tiny window.

"Mr Read said I could have the milk thistles from the end of his
garden for Goldie . . . You won't forget?"

by Teresa Ashby.

Polly had felt a little hurt as she'd driven home. All the other children
had been hugging their parents goodbye, but all Lucy could think about
was her rabbit.

"Second place in her affections behind a rabbit." Mike had laughed
when she'd told him. "Oh, dear."

"Third," Polly had said grumpily. "Don't forget she's her daddy's blue-
eyed girl."

64

Illustration by Sally Rowe.

Mike had reached for her hand sympathetically.

"Aren't all girls at that age? Polly, you know she thinks of you as her mother."

It hadn't been easy, stepping into someone else's shoes and taking on a two-year-old but, over the years, Polly and Lucy had become friends.

In fact, although it had been Mike who'd brought the rabbit home, it had been Polly's idea.

65

She was a pretty little thing, with golden fur and bright brown eyes, and Lucy adored her. She never tired of her and loved to tell her new brother, Daniel, all about Goldie's antics.

And now, Polly thought, as she looked into the hutch, she'd lost her!

She could get another rabbit, but Lucy would know the difference immediately. Goldie was so tame, she didn't act like a rabbit at all.

She liked to be cuddled in Lucy's arms, lying upside down on her back like a baby. She even came into the house and curled up next to the dog — Sally seemed to have adopted her as a surrogate pup.

There was no way Polly would be able to replace Goldie without Lucy knowing.

And, worse still, she had to tell Mike.

She hurried back to the house where Mike was eating breakfast.

"Wonder how Lucy's getting on," he mused. "I remember *my* first time away from home. It was a great adventure, but I was glad to be back."

"Me, too," Polly said. "Mike, about Goldie —"

"Oh, you remembered to feed her? Good for you. Lucy would be heartbroken if anything happened to the little rabbit while she was away."

Polly swallowed the lump in her throat and was about to confess all when Mike spoke again.

"She wouldn't trust anyone but you to take care of her. Not even me. That must tell you something."

Perhaps, Polly thought, it would be wise to tell Mike later. Maybe Goldie would be home by then! Unless she'd found the patch of milk thistles in Mr Read's garden . . .

"Look at the time! I've got to dash. See you later, love!" Mike pecked her cheek and ruffled his son's hair before hurrying out.

Polly looked at Daniel, who was sitting in his high chair, banging his spoon and laughing.

"It's all right for you to laugh," she said. "You haven't lost Lucy's rabbit!"

Daniel thought this was hilarious and whacked his spoon into his porridge, sending a stream up in the air. Most of it landed on Polly.

She sighed. Oh, the joys of motherhood!

Then Daniel lifted his spoon to his mouth and plunged it between his lips. He gave her a great, happy smile.

"Oh, you clever boy!" Polly cried. "Clever, clever boy!"

And to prove just how clever he was, Daniel managed to get another spoonful into his mouth before the bowl went spinning to the floor.

Polly had missed Lucy's early years. When she'd met Mike, Lucy was two — a walking, talking, mini-tornado. Mike had been newly-divorced and coping admirably with a demanding job and looking after his daughter.

How any mother could leave her child was beyond Polly. And now, as she wiped porridge from her face and looked at her beaming son, the love she felt for both children strengthened.

They were a family — she and Mike and Lucy and Daniel. A family with all the usual ups and downs.

So of course she could tell Mike about the rabbit tonight.

A S they ate dinner, Mike looked at Lucy's empty place and heaved a sigh.

"It's not the same without her," he remarked. "The house seems too quiet."

"Mike, about Goldie . . ." Polly began as Mike reached for the potatoes.

"Yes?" He smiled at her. "Lucy loves that rabbit, doesn't she? Remember I made her promise that if she had a rabbit, she'd have to look after it? Well, she certainly has."

He wasn't making this easy for her.

"Feeding her, cleaning her out, scrounging milk thistles and clover from Mr Read. And Goldie loves the attention she gives her, doesn't she?"

"She does, but —"

"Hard to believe she's had her for two years. I thought rabbits didn't live all that long, but someone was telling me they had one for ten years!"

"Ten years." Polly gulped.

"She'll grow up with Goldie," Mike said. "Brings a lump to your throat just thinking about it."

Polly turned to gaze out of the window. She could hear the distant rumble of a train and the hum of traffic on the not-so-distant dual carriageway. Apart from these dangers, there were foxes in the wood and the big neighbourhood cats.

Poor Goldie wouldn't stand a chance!

Polly let out a tiny sob.

"Aw, you're missing her, too, aren't you, love?"

Polly managed to nod — how could she tell him that more than anything she was absolutely dreading Lucy coming home?

She'd never forgive her.

All those years spent building a relationship with her stepdaughter would be forgotten. Polly would be the one who lost Goldie and broke Lucy's heart.

She didn't tell Mike in the end. When he went to bed she shone a torch hopefully around the garden but, apart from a couple of foraging hedgehogs, the garden was as empty as Goldie's hutch.

There were two more days before Lucy would be home and while Mike was at work, Polly practised what she would tell Lucy on her return. She'd be honest with her.

She'd been careless. She'd left the hutch door open and Goldie had escaped. But saying that Goldie had escaped might make Lucy think the rabbit hadn't been happy here.

If she said he'd been stolen, Lucy would be even more upset.

Oh, it was so difficult!

Polly spent hours in the garden, searching in vain. And she did try to tell Mike what had happened — but the words stuck in her throat.

IN the end, it was Mr Read, Polly's neighbour, who made the best suggestion. He appeared on the doorstep the day Lucy was due home.

"You haven't called round for the thistles," he said, handing over a bag full of greenery. "I promised your little girl she could have some. There are some carrot tops in there as well, and a bit of clover."

Mike was at work, Daniel was out with his granny and Polly was at the end of her tether. When she saw the thistles, she burst into tears.

Mr Read stepped backwards, put out.

"Was it something I said?"

"Goldie's gone." Polly sobbed. "I must have left the hutch door open . . . She's run away."

"Oh, dear," Mr Read said, scratching his chin. "And when's Lucy due back?"

"This afternoon." Polly sniffed. "She'll never forgive me."

"Have you tried luring the rabbit back?"

"What?" She blinked at her neighbour, puzzled.

"Putting food in her hutch. She's very tame, I should imagine she'd keep coming home and checking on things."

Polly blinked. She'd never thought of that.

"Do you think it would work?"

"It's worth a try. Come on. Let's put some food in the hutch and see what happens."

The Peat Fire Flame

WHEN the snows of winter fell,
Neighbours to the ceilidh cam
Gathering round the hearth to tell
Stories by the peat-fire flame . . .

Legends handed down of old,
Fairy music, pipers gay —
Tales to make the blood run cold;
Ghosts that haunt by night and day!

Some told how an ancient crone
Turned herself into a hare;
Some described a loch, well-known,
Where a kelpie had his lair.

Folk with second sight might then
Warn of hazards yet to be,
Others tell of fishermen
Wedding mermaids from the sea.

Timeless tales to warm the heart,
Driving out the winter chill.
Now, alas, a dying art,
Yet their magic haunts us still!
— *Brenda G. Macro*

Polly made a cup of coffee while Mr Read arranged carrot tops and thistles in Goldie's hutch. Then he came into the kitchen and they sat down at the table together.

"What now?"

"We wait," he explained. "If she's anywhere near, she'll be back soon."

"Do you really think it's possible?"

"Yes. She loves that little girl. She wouldn't want to escape."

"But the lure of the great outdoors and freedom . . ."

"If that rabbit has any sense, she'll be back. Once she's run from a fox and the Sandersons' old black cat, and maybe had one or two near misses on the road, she'll realise which side her bread is buttered."

They finished their coffee and Mr Read polished off the last of the cake Polly had made the day before.

"Let's see, shall we?" Mr Read said finally, reaching for his cap.

When they stepped into the garden, Polly couldn't believe her eyes. There, in the middle of the lawn, sniffing the daisies, was a furry golden blob.

"What did I tell you?" Mr Read whispered gleefully.

"Shall I catch her?"

"No, no." He put a restraining hand on her arm. "Watch."

Sure enough, Goldie ambled over to her hatch and jumped up.

"Now!"

Polly sprinted down the garden and closed the door.

Goldie didn't even notice, she was so busy munching.

"Mr Read . . . no-one else knows about this," Polly said rather awkwardly.

"No-one will hear about it from me," he promised, giving her a wide smile.

Later that day, Mike and Polly took Daniel to meet Lucy.

She was first off the bus and came tearing towards them, arms open wide.

She'll ask about Goldie, Polly thought, and I'll be able to tell her she's fine! She'll probably hug her dad first —

But it was Polly's arms she flung herself into.

"Oh, Mum! I've missed you!" she cried. "You, too, Dad! And you, Stinky!" She gave her little brother a big kiss and he laughed up at her. "How's Goldie?"

"Goldie's fine," Mike assured her. "She missed you, though."

"Oh . . . oh, yes, she certainly has," Polly whispered.

"I knew you'd look after her, Mum," Lucy said and her faith in Polly was so deep, so touching, that Polly felt tears come to her eyes.

ABOUT a month later, something strange happened. Goldie, who had seemed to put on weight since her adventure, suddenly produced four babies.

Mike and Lucy were absolutely baffled.

Mr Read was the expert on rabbits and was invited round to witness the phenomenon. He shook his head and managed to look as puzzled as the rest of them.

"Remarkable," he said. "But I couldn't tell you how this happened, not a bit."

Then he looked at Polly and gave her a wink, his face fighting to suppress a grin.

Polly couldn't tell either — not ever!

Goldie's miracle would have to remain one of life's mysteries. ■

A Fair Exchange

by Susan Smith.

THE spring sunshine was flooding in through the classroom windows as Fran did a brief tour of inspection, admiring the childrens' artwork on the walls.

After six months' absence, she felt like a new girl. It had been strange to sit in the staffroom again; she'd felt quite shy drinking coffee with all her old friends and facing the barrage of questions. It was nice to now be on her own for a few minutes, in her own room.

The teachers had clubbed together to buy her a large bunch of flowers and she placed them in a water jug on her desk, then sat down and let her mind wander back to the last time she'd sat there. So much had happened — it was as if she was a completely different person.

What had that Fran Barlow, who had sat here this time last year, been like?

She opened the desk drawers, one after another. They were all empty except for the bottom one,

Illustration by Mike Heslop.

which held a pile of her old personal papers.

There were rough plans for lessons and projects, old timetables and a couple of magazines for reading in the lunch hour. And there, at the bottom, a sheet of details from a local estate agent.

Lilac Cottage, Lovers Lane.

She found herself smiling as she read the brief description.

Detached stone cottage in idyllic, peaceful position in quiet country lane. In need of some renovation, which is reflected in the price.

She had seen the cottage advertised in the estate agents' window and gone in to make an appointment to view right away. It was just what she and Richard had been dreaming of — somewhere out of town, with a large, private garden for the children to play in.

The children were dreams, too, but they were both quite sure about the future.

First — find the right house. Richard was adamant that it should be something they could afford on just his pay, so that Fran would not need to work for a few years.

Then they'd start a family . . .

With Richard being the only child of elderly parents, who had died several years before, Fran knew how important the idea of a family was to him.

Luckily she loved children, too. And her parents were delighted at the thought of grandchildren to adore and spoil!

They had gone along to Lilac Cottage on a perfect late May day and had leaned on the garden wall in the evening sunshine. The two large trees which gave the cottage its name had been in full bloom and the scent had been beautiful.

Richard had wrestled with the rather rusty lock, then stared in dismay at the crumbling plaster and rotting window frame in the front room.

"The walls would all have to be re-plastered — but there's no sign of damp. I like the fireplace."

They'd stood and admired the old brick hearth with a huge oak beam for a mantelpiece then walked through into the large dining/kitchen.

"What kitchen?" Richard had said, glancing at an old rusty cooker, a cracked sink and a couple of rather woebegone cupboards.

Fran's heart had sunk as they'd climbed upstairs, listening to Richard explain how expensive it would be to replace all the windows.

"It would be a crime to put in cheap ones. You'd have to have some made just like the originals, otherwise the whole character of the place would be spoiled."

She'd agreed but, oh, she so wanted this cottage! It had felt just right — as though it had been waiting for them to turn it into a home again.

Upstairs in the bathroom they'd both stared in silence at the enormous, claw-footed iron bath. It was badly stained.

"Well, this is one room we won't have to spend much on," Richard had

A Fair Exchange

said with a grin. "I've never liked modern, tiled bathrooms. We can just resurface the bath and paint the panelling. What colour do you fancy?"

With a grateful sigh, Fran had followed him into the big front bedroom.

"Do you really like it as much as I do, Richard?"

He'd given her a huge bear-hug.

"It isn't perfect, love — but it will be. A perfect family home."

THE bell rang to call the school to Assembly and Fran hurriedly pushed Lilac Cottage to the back of the drawer.

As she walked into the hall with the other teachers, she thought how much had changed in less than a year. How much older, and wiser, she was . . .

Mrs McKenzie, the headmistress, walked into the hall at nine o'clock precisely. She was a great believer in setting the children a good example about punctuality.

Fran took her old seat at the ancient but well-polished, upright piano and played the opening bars of the morning hymn, "All Things Bright And Beautiful". A good start for the first day of a new term.

Then Mrs McKenzie stood up.

"Welcome back, everyone. I hope you've all had a good rest and have come back ready to work hard and enjoy the next few weeks.

"Before you go to your classrooms, I think we should say a special 'Welcome Back' to Miss Barlow, who has been away for six months. Can anyone tell me where she has been?"

A forest of hands shot into the air.

"To Toronto, Miss," Sophie from class three said proudly. "In Canada."

Mrs McKenzie nodded approvingly.

"That's right. Miss Barlow has been teaching children in Toronto. And we had Miss Duval with us, telling us all about life in Canada — which was very interesting.

"It's what is called an 'exchange visit'. And we're very glad to have Miss Barlow back with us again. Except that we haven't really got Miss Barlow back at all!"

The children all craned their heads to look at Fran. Most of them were quite puzzled, but a few had knowing looks — in a small town there were few secrets.

Mrs McKenzie laughed.

"While Miss Barlow was teaching in Canada, she got married. She is Mrs Hamilton! So, as well as welcoming her back, we must congratulate her, and hope that she and Mr Hamilton will be very happy together."

There was a burst of applause and Fran felt all eyes on her. She smiled round, self-consciously, and was relieved when the headmistress called for, "eyes closed, hands together", and launched into the two simple prayers which always started the day.

A TRIP to the islands of Mull and Iona always seems a great adventure. It's a twisting road to drive through Morven, to cross from Lochaline to Fishnish. But there is a shorter way — to catch the ferry from Oban to Craignure, or Tobermory.

However you arrive, you'll find a varied landscape and some incredibly narrow roads! What seems like a short journey on a map can take ages as you nip in and out of passing places to allow traffic to go the other way. But why hurry? There's plenty of lovely scenery to enjoy.

I found plenty of local produce in the islands' restaurants — everything from the beef in the steak pie to the lobster, crab, prawns and oysters.

And if you enjoy picnics, like me, you'll be spoilt for choice. There's nothing like a chunk of award-winning Mull Cheddar Cheese, accompanied by locally-made chutney and bread. And I never forget to include some Isle Of Mull shortbread in my basket, or Tobermory Chocolate. I picked my favourites in the chocolate factory shop in Tobermory.

The little island of Iona can seem a world away from bustling Tobermory. It's a beautiful, tranquil place, with white beaches and a vivid green sea.

Walking off the ferry, you're sure to smell baking as you pass a tiny bakehouse which serves a bar and restaurant at the pier head. I was

Tobermory Chocolate.

After a busy morning getting to know everyone again, Fran was glad of the lunchtime break. She volunteered to do playground duty and left the other teachers looking through her wedding photographs in the staffroom.

It was a relief to be alone with her thoughts for a while. She managed to prevent two small boys from strangling a third with his own scarf and, turning her coat collar up against the blustery wind, began to walk round the playground.

She looked at the ring gleaming on her left hand. Mrs Fran Hamilton. With all her dreams last summer, she'd certainly never thought of going to Canada — or of getting married so soon.

It was Mrs McKenzie who had started it all. Fran smiled — she was a most unlikely Cupid.

Mull and Iona

Iona fishermen.

Dennis Hardley.

...nce told you could buy Scotland's best scones ...ere!

You could be lucky ...nough to see fishermen ...t work on their creels. ...t's a skilled job but there is a little luck involved, too. Baiting an old creel which he had mended with string, my brother managed to land a lobster while he was working on the island one summer. I had no such luck but, watching the sun set over the sea with a small nip of Tobermory Whisky, I couldn't have wished for a better day.

From her first day at St Andrew's Primary she had known nothing but kindness and support from the tall, energetic lady who ran her school so well. She believed in discipline.

"Above all, children like to know who's in charge, who they can turn to. They need that, and they respect a firm hand."

She was right. As a young teacher, fresh from training college, Fran had quickly realised that her real training began in the school and that she could not have had a better start to her career.

It had been the day after their offer on Lilac Cottage was accepted that Mrs McKenzie had shown her the letter from Canada. It was from the headmistress of a school in a small town outside Toronto, that was twinned with their own.

"I think it would be an excellent idea for St Andrew's. It would give the children an insight into how other children live and learn.

"And I think it would be valuable for you, too, Fran. It would give you lots of new ideas that you could bring back and share with us. What do you think?"

Fran herself had agreed, excited at the thought of six months in Canada. Winter months, too — with all that snow!

It had never seriously crossed her mind that Richard would object to delaying their plans.

He'd listened to her very quietly.

"I don't think you should go, Fran. Not now, when we've got all our plans made for the cottage. If we delay, someone else will snap it up.

"Just tell the Head to ask someone else. She'll understand."

It was Fran who didn't understand. How could Richard — who was always so reasonable and considerate — not see how important this was to her?

It had been a dreadful row, escalating, as rows do, and ending in a terrible ultimatum.

"If you go, Fran, that's it as far as I'm concerned. It's your choice — me and the cottage, or this silly trip."

Fran had poured it all out to Mrs McKenzie the next day.

"So that's it. Could you write back and accept? And ask them to arrange accommodation for me from September?"

She'd seen the concern on Mrs McKenzie's face.

"I've made my mind up," she'd explained. "I really want to do this and, if Richard is so selfish that he won't see it from my point of view, then it's as well I found out now, before it's too late."

Brave words, but she hadn't felt very brave a few weeks later as she'd waited with her luggage at the airport. Although she'd been determined not to give in, she'd still hoped Richard might turn up to see her off.

She hadn't heard from him since the row, but she'd looked in the estate agents' window and seen that Lilac Cottage had been sold.

She'd blinked the tears away. If Richard had really thought so much of her, he wouldn't have let her go so easily . . .

As she'd taken her seat on the plane, she'd made a resolution to forget all about him and Lilac Cottage. She'd concentrate on putting her heart and soul into her Canadian adventure and enjoy it as much as she could.

* * * *

As she lined the children up to go back into school, Fran caught the gleam of her ring and smiled happily to herself. She'd been so lucky!

The afternoon passed quickly. Fran had brought back a scrapbook that the Canadian children had made about their country. There were pictures of wild flowers and animals and short essays about holidays and pastimes.

She suggested a competition, with the best essays and drawings to be made into a scrapbook about St Andrew's, which she would send off to Canada.

By the end of the day, the children were eager to be off, but Fran stayed for almost an hour. She was catching up on paperwork, when she saw the familiar, rather elderly, red car waiting in the carpark.

She hurried outside, calling a goodbye to the caretaker. As she sank gratefully into the front passenger seat, she sighed theatrically.

"Oh, that's a relief. It was good to be back but I'm exhausted. All the questions!

"'Was it good to be back home?', 'What was Canada really like?', 'How did the wedding go?', 'How long was the flight?'"

She looked at Richard — her Richard — and laughed.

"Don't dare ask me any questions tonight. Not even 'What's for tea?'!"

As Richard concentrated on negotiating his way through the traffic, she thought again how lucky she'd been. Before the plane had touched down in Toronto, she'd admitted her own selfishness. The first thing she'd done on Canadian soil was to ring Richard from a payphone at the airport.

He'd admitted that he had felt exactly the same! In fact, he'd already written to her, saying that he understood how much the exchange visit meant and that he would wait for her. And that Lilac Cottage would be waiting, too.

By the end of the phone call, he'd proposed. They'd both known he'd be coming to Canada, too . . .

RICHARD parked the car carefully on the grass verge and lifted her briefcase up from the back seat.

"I'm sure you've heard this before today, many times. But welcome back, love!"

They stood for a moment, looking up at the cottage. The lilac trees weren't in bloom yet, but the narcissi and primulas made a lovely display — if you ignored the pile of builders' rubble under the new window!

"Are you sure you don't regret the way we've had to change our plans?" she asked softly.

Fran's parents had insisted on paying for the wedding and had combined it with a retirement holiday, driving down to Niagara and New England afterwards. But the cost of Richard's flight and their honeymoon had made quite a hole in their savings. She was going to have to work for a couple of years until they finished renovating the cottage.

Richard shook his head firmly.

"No, love. I know we'll have to wait a little longer to start a family, but we had a wonderful honeymoon that we'll always remember. And we'll appreciate Lilac Cottage all the more if we get the work done slowly."

He looked round at the rather bare kitchen and pulled her into his arms.

"I reckon it's been a very fair exchange." ■

Wish upon A Star

"G RAN, look at this! It's beautiful!" Kate's voice was filled with excitement, as it had been for much of December.

Rosemary made her way into the living-room.

Kate was marooned on an island of carpet, with a wide sea of cardboard and tissue all round her. She beamed as she held up her latest find — a silver star, made out of a coat hanger, frilly with tinsel.

"It's so pretty. Is it yours? It looks old."

"It's not *that* old." Rosemary stroked it.

"Grandad made it for Daddy, when he was about your age. We had it on the tree right until he grew up." She turned it in her hands and smiled. "It would have looked a bit silly on the little tree we had after that."

78

Illustration by Ian Thurston.

by Lynne Barrett-Lee.

"But now we're all living together we're going to get the biggest tree in Britain," Kate said gravely, "so it will look just right on the top. Don't you think, Gran?"

Rosemary smiled.

"It's special, you know," she told Kate. "It was Daddy's wishing star."

"Then I'm going to wish for some snow. I want heaps and heaps of it for Christmas Day — so it had better start snowing quickly." Kate cuddled Rosemary's arm and gazed at the star.

"What will you wish for, Gran? Or are you and Grandad too old to have wishes?"

"No way!" Rosemary protested. "Far from it."

79

For while she and Ted could look back on 40 wonderful years together, Stephen and Carolyn had enjoyed barely five before that senseless accident had left him to bring up his daughter alone.

Rosemary looked down at Kate's curly head and was filled with relief that they'd been able to move back to the farm from their retirement cottage on the coast. For a few years at least, they were needed back here.

Rosemary could never take the place of Kate's mother, but she was only too happy to be there with her granddaughter, allowing Stephen, with Ted's help, to manage the farm.

They'd been back almost six months now, and Kate was positively blooming.

If Rosemary could have just one wish granted, it would be for Stephen to realise there still might be happiness for him. For something, no, *someone,* to fill the void in his life, and help him to feel hopeful again.

When was the last time she'd heard Stephen laugh — *really* laugh, not just for Kate's benefit?

H AVE you wished yet?" Kate tugged her arm, and Rosemary smiled. There was the girl that Stephen had just started seeing — the daughter of one of her friends . . . Tonight was the third time they'd been out lately . . .

"I've wished."

"For what?"

"It's a secret. You shouldn't tell wishes, or they might not come true."

"But what about the snow?"

Rosemary saw her mistake.

"Don't worry. Just wish again, in your head. Now, look at the time! I must get you to bed. What sort of a babysitter will Dad think I am, keeping you up till this hour of the night?"

"Do you think it *will* snow?" Kate asked, as they made their way upstairs.

"We'll just have to see." Rosemary pulled back the edges of Kate's gingham curtains.

The night sky was clear, blue-black and spangled with pin-pricks of stars. A bright lemon moon lit the frost on the garden. Good for Ted, out delivering last-minute geese, but for Kate, disappointing — not a snow cloud in sight.

There was a storm cloud in the kitchen on the morning of Christmas Eve when Stephen finally came down for his breakfast.

Rosemary had been up for some time, anxious for news, but her son's face stopped her questions. She turned his bacon under the grill.

He stomped to the cooker and snatched up the kettle.

"Nice evening?" she ventured finally.

"Not particularly."

"Still," Rosemary went on, "it's good to get out. You spend far too much time stuck . . ."

Stephen wheeled around to face her.

"For goodness' sake, Mum! Can't you leave it for once?"

"I'm sorry, I just . . ."

"Well, don't just. OK? I'm getting tired of this obsession with my social life. I'm perfectly happy as I am." He turned to the kettle and Rosemary bit back her answer.

Stephen's usual cheerful face might convince Kate, but, inside, Rosemary knew he was just marking time. She'd hoped that once she and Ted had moved back, Stephen would be able to leave the farm more, but despite her encouragement, he turned down most of the invitations he got.

"I'm sorry," she said. "I don't mean to interfere. It's just — I worry about you, that's all."

"So much that you're happy to tell all and sundry I'm a poor, forlorn soul who's helpless without a woman to take care of him?" Stephen's anger was almost palpable, and Rosemary winced.

"Oh, yes," he went on. "Susan spelt it out for me. *You'd* told her mother I needed looking after! Don't bother denying it.

"And it isn't the first time, either, is it? Anyway, I won't be seeing her any more, so you can forget about any plans you may have had for us, OK?"

"But it wasn't like that. Susan's always been keen on you, Stephen —"

"She's keen, all right. To the point of suffocation. I'm not ill, Mum! I don't need a doe-eyed nurse to dote on me. One mother's quite enough, thanks." He stopped as Kate came in.

"Dad!" She rushed to her father and threw her arms around him. "One day till Christmas! Are you getting the tree today, Daddy?"

Stephen picked up his daughter, and Rosemary watched his eyes soften.

"Of course, sweetie. Grandad and I will go and fetch it just as soon as he gets home. Now, let's have some breakfast. I'd better get a move on and sort out the animals, and I'm sure you and Gran have got plenty to do."

He put Kate down and made himself tea while Rosemary served his cooked breakfast. She was, for once, thankful for Kate's interminable chatter as Stephen's disapproval hung over her.

Had she really told Susan so much? Well, she *had* interfered, and she'd upset him . . .

Stephen finished his meal.

"I'll be off, then." He stroked Kate's hair as he passed.

"Oh, Dad! Did Gran tell you? We're going to put your special star on the tree." Her eyes were shining with excitement.

Stephen looked puzzled. Then his face cleared.

"I'd forgotten about that." He smiled at Kate. "Made your wish yet?"

"Yes. It's — oh, no, sorry, I can't tell you, or it won't come true. And so has Gran. You and Grandad can make yours tonight."

Rosemary glanced up at the sky as Stephen left. Low cloud was massing at the tops of the hills, dulling their bright folds. Perhaps Kate, at least, would have her wish come true.

They spent the morning busily cooking. Mince-pies and sausage rolls baked in the range while outside the sky darkened. By midday the first flakes of snow began falling, a cotton-wool shower that speckled the ground.

Kate was ecstatic.

"My wish! It came true!" She danced round the table. "Can we go out and play in it? Will Dad and Grandad help me make a snowman?"

"Calm down. Grandad's got to get home first!" Rosemary glanced at the clock. "In fact, he should be halfway home already. Let's clear up and pop down to the village. See if we can get hold of some of Dad's favourite chocolates."

"He's sad today, isn't he, Gran?" Kate said suddenly. "Are they to help cheer him up?"

"Well, they might." Rosemary could have kicked herself for upsetting him in the first place. She'd wanted this Christmas to be a happy one . . .

"Let him be." She could hear Ted's voice now. "Steve's got to find his own way through this. He's not a child any more."

Kate's cheeks were two bright little spots of pale pink, and traces of flour touched the tips of her fringe.

"I'm so excited, Gran. I hope the snow gets really, really deep."

Rosemary brushed off her hair and then cuddled her tightly. Kate was happy, anyway, and that was the thing Stephen most cared about.

She opened the front door. A soft, fluffy eiderdown hugged the hard ground, and the air had that unmistakable stillness that meant more snow on the way. She took Kate's hand as they picked their way down the path.

"Do you know what?" she said. "I think it might. Let's hope Grandad gets home safely first."

BY the time they returned, the snow had drawn the whole landscape under its soft, crystal veil. The village had become a grey blur in the valley, and each branch, twig and stem was now fat with frosting.

Rosemary and Kate spent an energetic half hour sweeping the snow from the drive and the paths, before the bitter cold reddened their noses and they hurried back in to hot chocolate and toast.

Rosemary looked again at the old kitchen clock. Like so many things here, it had been hers for years, left for Stephen and Carolyn when she and Ted had retired . . .

Where *was* Ted? He should surely have arrived back by now.

Minutes later, Stephen appeared at the door, stamping snow from his boots and pulling off gloves. Rosemary scanned his face warily, but his smile was warm and untroubled. This morning's quarrel, she hoped, would be forgotten now.

"That's the animals all in. Dad not back yet?" He blew into cupped hands, then scooped up his daughter.

"The tree, Daddy! What have you done with the tree?"

"What tree was that?"

"Oh, Daddy! You didn't forget!"

"Oh, *that* tree!

The Spinner

SKILFULLY, her foot and hand
Work the wheel that twists the strand;
Spinning, till the day is spent,
Wool for many uses meant.

Yarn, by methods learned of yore,
Dyed with plants from hill and shore —
Heather, crotal, tansy gold,
Woven into patterns old.
Tartans casting still their spell,
Each with an ancient tale to tell,
Of old clan battles, lost or won,
Legends, tales, great deeds done.

Wool for knitting sweaters fine;
Fair Isle's intricate design;
Seamen's jerseys, dark and warm,
Proof against the winter storm;
Gloves and mufflers; hose and tweeds —
Comforts every crofter needs —
All from snowy fleeces start,
Transformed by the spinner's art!
— *Brenda G. Macrow.*

W. Shand.

83

Outside. It's too big to fit in the house," he teased her gently.

"But, Daddy . . ."

"Don't be daft, Kate," Rosemary chipped in. "Daddy will trim it. Now let him sit down and get a hot drink inside him." She turned to Stephen.

"I'm getting a little worried about your father," she murmured. "I hope he's not stranded somewhere."

Stephen shook his head.

"He'll be fine, Mum. Don't worry."

But by the time the tree was up, two hours later, Rosemary couldn't help worrying. She was stationed at the living-room window, her mind out in the snowdrift she could imagine Ted stuck in.

"Come on, Gran," Kate called. "Come and help. Make sure you put some lights at the back, Daddy!"

"What for? No-one can see them round there."

"For Santa Claus, silly! Or he won't see the cottage! He doesn't have any maps, you know!"

Stephen sat back on his heels and chuckled.

"I don't know. You get more like your grandmother every day, Kate! Bossy boots, that's what you are."

Rosemary was about to tell him what she thought of that when a dim wash of yellow in the distance caught her eye. The van at last!

"Hurry up with that tree, Kate. Grandad's home." She crossed the room in four strides. A bitter wind slapped at her face as she opened the front door.

"Hurry up, Ted!" she called into the darkness.

But it wasn't her husband running towards her, it was a girl, huddled in ski jacket and hat. Incongruously, she was holding a basket of flowers, an exuberant display of cheerful blooms.

Rosemary's surprise must have shown, because the girl grinned as she held them out.

"Mrs Carter? I thought I recognised you, from church. These are for you. Merry Christmas and . . . er . . . ho, ho, ho!"

"Yes, of course. You're Fiona from Fiona's Flowers! You help with the flowers in church, don't you? But, who on earth . . .?" Rosemary, took the basket.

"Well, the card says 'to Mum' so I guess he's your son . . . Anyway, I must get going. It was bad enough getting here. Goodness knows what it'll be like getting back!"

She waved, and headed for her van before Stephen came out. He peered into the distance.

"No Dad? Oh, the flowers have come . . . I can't believe she delivered them in this weather."

"Well, she did, and they're beautiful, but you shouldn't have, Stephen."

"I should. I was awful to you this morning. I know you mean well,

Mum. I shouldn't have lost my temper with you."

"And I should learn to keep my mouth shut, shouldn't I? I don't deserve these, but it certainly won't stop me from enjoying them."

He gave her a rare kiss, and they moved back to the living-room.

Moments later, the doorbell brought them back to the hall.

"Not Dad — he's got his key." Stephen pulled the door open to find Fiona outside again.

"I'm sorry," she said. "You don't happen to have a shovel I could borrow, do you? Only I'm . . ."

"Stuck in the snow?" Stephen raised his eyebrows.

"Well and truly. But if you could lend me . . ."

"I can't say I'm surprised. I was just saying to my mother, it's reckless of you to come out on a night like this. The flowers could have waited . . . what on earth possessed you?"

Rosemary watched Fiona's chin jut as she answered.

"You, mainly," she said levelly. "You said they were important."

"But that was this morning, before it snowed! You could have been hurt," Stephen protested.

Fiona turned to Rosemary.

"*Do* you have a spare shovel?"

"Of course, dear. It's right here in the porch . . ."

"Hang on. I'll help you." Stephen picked up his coat.

"There's no need. I'm perfectly capable." Fiona's voice was as frosty as the air. She turned and smiled at Rosemary.

"Thank you so much for the shovel, Mrs Carter. I'll make sure I get it back to you."

She gave Stephen a glare and stomped off into the night.

"Well? Go after her, then!" Rosemary rounded on Stephen.

"She doesn't seem to want any help," Stephen said.

"I'm not surprised, after the way you spoke to her! But we can't leave her out there on her own."

Rosemary watched as he jogged off in pursuit. Ted could well be stuck in this lot somewhere. She went into the kitchen and boiled the kettle for hot drinks, then returned to Kate, who was now entangled in tinsel.

THEY had barely finished stringing the lights before a bobbing torch signalled Stephen's return. Fiona was still with him, and Rosemary went out to meet them. They were still at odds.

"It's out of the question," Stephen was saying firmly. "Isn't it, Mum? Fiona wants to walk back down to the village, and I've told her she mustn't. The snow's on again. Unless . . ." He stopped.

"Unless what?" Fiona's tone was equally firm. Here, for a change, was a woman who couldn't give two hoots for Stephen's opinion.

"Unless you let me come with you."

"I'd rather sleep in the van!"

Rosemary felt it was time she stepped in.

"Look, Fiona, this is really my fault. If I hadn't started an argument with Stephen this morning, he wouldn't have asked you to bring me the flowers.

"So you can imagine how I feel. And with my husband not back yet, I've quite enough to worry about without the pair of you tramping through a blizzard.

"I know you'd rather be at home, Fiona, but please, see reason.

"Spend the night with us. Stephen will see you home first thing. Won't you?"

Stephen nodded, and Fiona's face softened. Their eyes met and held for a lingering moment, a trace of a smile playing around Stephen's lips.

"Please stay," said a little voice from the living-room door. "Or we'll never get this finished before Santa Claus comes."

"Oh, Kate!" Stephen laughed, a genuine laugh, the sort Rosemary had longed to hear, and Fiona couldn't help joining in.

* * * *

"So, did you make all your wishes?" Fiona asked Kate a while later, after phone calls and hot drinks and mince-pies.

Kate smiled at her father and passed him a bauble.

"That one's best," Fiona said in passing, and Kate laughed as he obediently followed Fiona's orders.

"I wished all right, only Grandad's not here yet, and I think it's my fault. He's probably stuck in some snow up the mountain." He shook his head, frowning anxiously.

"Of course it's not your fault," Rosemary began, but at that moment the phone shrilled in the hall. She ran out to answer it.

"Ted! At last!"

"I doubt if you'll see me tonight, my love. I'm stuck this side of the hill, so I'm staying with John and Carol for the night. The forecast looks hopeful — I'll be back for Christmas lunch, I'm sure.

"And how's things at home? How's Kate bearing up?"

"She's not in bed yet. Too much excitement to sleep. But she got her snow."

Ted laughed.

"She did, an' all. Is everything OK?"

Rosemary peered into the lounge. All she could see were the backs of three heads, close together, examining a tree ornament. There was the murmur of voices, the soft tinkle of laughter. Laughter of a kind she'd not heard in a long time.

Stephen lifted Kate to place the wishing star on top of the tree, and Rosemary smiled to herself as she answered her husband.

"You know, Ted, I think everything is going to be fine." ∎

K AREN stared through the window at the cloud bank below. When the stewardess offered her a meal tray, she waved it away. She was too churned up to eat; all she could think about was Roger. Waking or sleeping, he filled her mind. Without him, she knew her life would seem so empty.

Even that first day, when he'd come into the store to buy perfume for his sister, there had been something about him. It was as if she already knew him.

He had come in every day after that until, at last, he'd persuaded her to have lunch with him.

That proved to be an hour filled with fun and laughter such as she

For My Sister's Sake

by Robyn Johns.

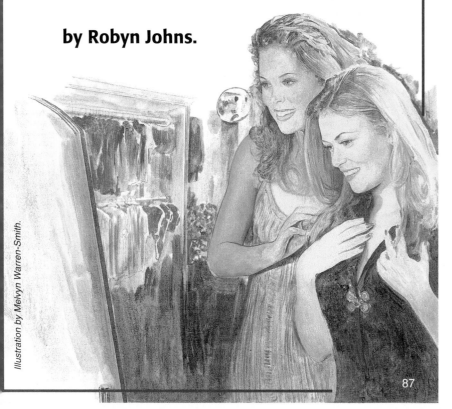

Illustration by Melvyn Warren-Smith.

had never known. She had never felt witty or amusing before but, with Roger Gale, suddenly she had been both.

Over the remains of their meal, he looked at her thoughtfully.

"Forgive me," he said politely. "But may I ask if there is one special person in your life?"

She returned his gaze steadily.

"Yes," she said. "My sister Mandy is very special. But if you're asking if I'm involved romantically — the answer is no."

His grin broadened.

"I wonder why that makes me feel so good?" he said.

Karen smiled, and decided to tell him about Mandy. There was something about Roger Gale that made her want to confide in him.

"I brought her up," she told him. "I was sixteen when Mother died and Mandy was twelve.

"Three years later, Dad died. I don't think she's ever got over it." Karen sipped her coffee.

"She's away at the moment. She wants to be an actress and talked herself into a job with a play on tour. But she'll soon come home to try something else. I have to make sure she has a secure home base."

They walked through the Knightsbridge crowds to the staff entrance and Roger asked her out to the theatre with him the following night.

Karen had vowed never to become involved in anything that might threaten Mandy's security. But Roger was only a passing tourist, Mandy was away — what possible harm could there be in a night out?

The theatre was packed, and Karen adored the show. She had meant to say goodbye to him after dinner, but it had been a perfect evening and it seemed ungrateful.

She surprised herself by inviting him back for a drink.

In the flat he sank down on the sofa with a sigh of content while she made some coffee.

"This is nice," he said. "You have some magnificent furniture here."

"Most of it belonged to our parents. For Mandy's sake I wanted to keep as much as I could."

"You seem very close to your sister." He gave her that searching look she was beginning to know.

"I'm certainly responsible for her," she said. "Besides —"

"Besides what?"

"Well — I promised Dad I'd look after her."

They talked until the small hours and Karen felt she had never been truly herself with anyone until now. Roger seemed to accept her exactly the way she was.

They saw a lot of one another during the next couple of weeks. There were yellow roses. There was a candlelit dinner.

Karen blossomed and loved every moment she spent in his company. For the first and only time in her life, she was putting herself before Mandy.

Somewhere at the back of her mind she knew Roger's holiday would end, but for now she just lived for the moment.

Suddenly, it was their last day together. Over a long lunch they tried to make light of it, but the misery of their parting was just beneath the surface.

"You never did go out of London, did you?" Karen said. "What happened to Scotland and Wales?"

"Some other time. I'm happy enough with the way I've spent this vacation."

He gathered her in his arms.

"You know I'd stay if I could," he murmured into her hair. "But there's a heap of people over there who depend on me."

"I know." Her throat ached with the effort not to cry. "I understand."

As they drove to the airport, Roger promised to phone every day. While they waited at check-in, he held her hand in an iron grip.

All too soon his flight was called, and she could do nothing but watch him walk out of her life.

WHEN she opened the front door of the flat, her way was barred by a mountain of luggage and Mandy rushed out of the kitchen.

"Isn't it marvellous?" she said. "Terry gave me a lift and saved me hours on the beastly train."

"Terry?" Karen repeated. She was still dazed.

"Yes. The show ended last night — I left a message on the answer phone. Where have you been? You look terrible."

"I'm fine," she said briskly. "And it's lovely to have you home. I'll unpack this lot while you have a bath."

She threw herself into a frenzy of activity. Taking refuge in her familiar role, the pain of Roger's departure receded a little.

Eventually Mandy came into the living-room, vigorously towelling her hair.

"By the way, who's Terry?" Karen asked casually.

"He's this marvellous stage manager we had. He's quite a dish, actually." She looked into the mirror and smiled. "He's got a bit of a thing for me."

"But who is he? Is he all right?"

Mandy laughed.

"Honestly, Karen. Of course he's all right — and even if he wasn't, I could handle him."

Karen felt the old anxieties beginning to stir.

"It's so good to be home." Mandy flopped down beside her. "You've no idea what bliss this flat is after those foul digs. I don't know what I'd do if I didn't have you."

Karen thought of Roger, halfway over the Atlantic by this time.

She looked down at her sister. At least she was still happy — her home base was secure.

Perhaps in time she would get used to this feeling that half of herself had been torn away.

As the weeks went by, every song on the radio about separation and hopeless love seemed to be written just for Karen.

She was worried about Mandy, too, who hadn't found work and was preoccupied. Mandy would shut herself in her room, talking for hours on the phone.

MANDY only came to life when, by accident, she answered the phone to Roger. They hit it off at once and, from the first, had long conversations that left them roaring with laughter.

Karen was surprised, even a little jealous.

"Mandy sounds like a lot of fun," Roger said, when Karen finally took the phone. "I'd sure like to meet her." Karen knew she must stop Roger phoning her. They stood no chance of getting over each other while they stayed in contact. Yet she couldn't bring herself to end something that made her so happy.

Then, like a bolt from the blue, she was summoned to head office.

Because of her remarkable sales figures, she had been chosen to head a promotion at a Fifth Avenue store! New York wasn't Atlanta, but surely they could meet, and she could say what she was determined to say to Roger . . .

She called him that night to tell him.

"Great," he said. "The minute your promotion ends, nip on a plane to Atlanta and I'll meet you at the airport."

Of course, she ought to have warned him then that the only reason for coming was to end things. But she couldn't bear to take that joy out of his voice. And the thought of being with him swept everything else from her mind.

At first Roger and Karen were as happy in Atlanta as they had been in

Stirling Castle

THIS is an exciting time to visit the castle on the rock which broods over Stirling. Historic Scotland is painstakingly reconstructing the Palace at its heart, showing it as it was in its glory days. The Great Hall, its fresh stone a startling contrast to the rest, lets us see what the whole castle was like when new. Soon we'll be able to visit Palace rooms hung as they were for James V, with the famous Stirling Head carvings back in place. You can already see the kitchens as they were. And the views from the walls are superb!

STIRLING CASTLE: J. CAMPBELL KERR.

London. Roger was so proud of her as he introduced her to his friends. They made her welcome, saying how pleased they were that Roger had found someone special at last.

The glossy, sky-reflecting buildings of the city took her breath away.

"I've never seen anywhere like it," she said.

"Atlanta sure is a wonderful place," he said proudly. "You could find that out for yourself if you came to live here."

O N their last evening, they sat on the back porch in the gathering dusk.

"Do you like this house?" he asked her.

"Roger! How can you ask? It's beautiful."

"I've often asked myself why I bought it," he said. "But now, with you here — it seems so right. It's been waiting for us — for us to start our life together!"

Reality hit Karen like a bucket of water. She must put a stop to this now, or it wouldn't be fair on any of them.

Her throat felt dry.

"That would have been wonderful . . ." she said huskily — but Roger took her hands.

"I knew it that first day. That's why I kept coming back to the store. You feel the same, don't you? Tell me I haven't got it wrong."

"No, of course you haven't. I love being here with you — but it's impossible. I have to think of Mandy. I can't leave her. I told you that."

"I know what you told me, but, honey, you're wrong. I'm asking you to marry me. You can't ruin things for us both because of your misplaced loyalties."

Karen looked at him blankly.

"Misplaced? What do you mean?"

"I mean Mandy doesn't need you as much as you think."

"Of course she does!" She pulled her hands away. "Anyway, how can you say that? You've not even met her."

"I don't *have* to meet her. If I hadn't learned all this from you, the phone conversations would have been enough to tell me she's a sharp little cookie. She knows her way around.

"And I'll tell you something else, of the two of you, she's the survivor."

"It doesn't alter the fact I promised my parents I'd take care of her," Karen said coldly.

"Oh, Karen! Wake up! They didn't mean you had to stay with her until you were both little old ladies. I'm quite sure they wouldn't want you to ruin your own life."

"I made them a promise," she said stubbornly. "And however much I might want to, I'm not going back on it. Surely you can understand that? Or is it different over here? Do American men expect women to throw up everything and come running? Is that it?"

He looked at her coldly for the first time.

"No," he said. "That isn't it. This isn't just because of Mandy, is it? I believe you're afraid."

"Afraid of what?"

"Of making a commitment. 'Taking care of my sister' is your defence against the world. It stops you having to get too close to anyone else."

"You're being ridiculous," she snapped, furious with him now. "And what gives you the right to invent absurd psychological theories? It has nothing whatsoever to do with you."

He looked as though she had hit him, and for a moment she wanted to take it back. But she didn't. If it took this to end it, then so be it. In the morning she would leave. It would all be behind them.

At the airport they behaved like strangers. Karen had been awake all night, and she felt sick and helpless. She couldn't bear leaving him like this. He wasn't angry with her any more — he simply looked crushed and defeated.

She turned to catch his eye after they parted, but the crowd pushed her through the departure gate and she lost sight of him . . .

W HEN she let herself into the flat there were voices coming from Mandy's room. Karen went straight past to lie down on her bed. After a while the door burst open and Mandy came in with a mug of coffee, spilling much of it on the carpet.

"Karen — you're back! I want to hear everything. But first I've got to tell you *my* news." She paused, handing Karen the coffee.

"What news?" Karen asked faintly.

"Terry and I are going to be married."

Karen stared at her stupidly.

"Terry?" she said at last.

"Yes. He's been asking me since the tour finished. I didn't know what I felt and got into a state about it. But now I do know. I'm so happy, Karen!"

Impulsively, Mandy hugged her.

"Tell you what. I'll go and get him and you can let me know if big sister approves!"

When Mandy brought him in, Karen was still reeling under the shock. But she could see this lean, fair-haired young man with the open face and wide, generous smile adored Mandy.

"I'm sorry to spring this on you," Terry said. "And I can imagine what you must be feeling.

"But I want you to know that I intend to take the greatest possible care of Mandy — she's very special."

The more she watched them together, the more weight lifted from Karen's shoulders. They were so perfectly matched.

A ROUND almost every corner on Skye, you are faced with evidence of the island's colouful history. From the first settlers of 4000 years ago to its present position as a major tourist attraction, Skye is an eclectic mixture of the old and the new.

I've never been able to see it myself,

Chef Nick Nairn in action.

but many claim that the "Misty Isle's" outline, with its long peninsulas, resembles the shape of a lobster. It's certainly an apt shape; there's nowhere quite like Skye

for enjoying seafood.

Most recently I visited the island during the Skye and Lochalsh Food and Drink Festival, where I found a veritable culinary feast! It took place one week in

A Taste Of

A selection of locally produced foods.

Photographs courtesy of Skye & Lochalsh Enterprise.

When they left her alone, Karen lay back on her pillows, her head in a whirl.

Mandy was fine — she was a survivor — and Roger had been right.

Of the two of them it was Mandy who was looking ahead to a bright new future with the man she loved.

She swung her legs off the bed. What was the time difference between London and Atlanta? But maybe it was too late. She'd ended it . . .

While she was still thinking, the phone rang under her hand.

*   *   *   *

When the seatbelt sign came on Karen's legs felt like jelly. She remembered every single word of that phone call.

"Karen?" Roger's voice had been full of love and concern.

"Roger — we must talk."

"I know, honey. I've been doing a lot of thinking since you left. I know

94

Skye

September and was described as a celebration of local produce.

There was certainly plenty to celebrate! Sweet hill lamb, tender Highland beef, organically produced vegetables . . . the list is endless.

Wild mushrooms are also in abundance on Skye. I remember walking early one morning before breakfast and finding a field mushroom (of quite gigantic proportions). I duly took my find back to my bed and breakfast, where the accommodating landlady cooked it for my breakfast! A great start to any day!

For a wonderfully warming end to the day, a dram of whisky, once used by the Highland physicians to cure all manner of ills, can't be beaten. The word, whisky, derives from the Gaelic, uisge beatha, and means water of life.

Tallisker is Skye's most famous dram, of course. Lesser known, perhaps, are the Gaelic whiskies, produced by the company Praban na Linne, at Eilean Iarmain.

These are traditionally produced, and are labelled in the native tongue. This, it has been said, "greatly improves the flavour"! And who am I to argue with such logic?

you were only doing what you believed to be right — which is why I love you. Am I forgiven?"

"Yes, Roger — oh, yes!"

Breathlessly, she'd told him what had happened.

"What did I tell you? Mandy will be OK. Your folks can rest easy, because she has the two of us, plus a guy of her own to watch over her!"

Karen closed her eyes as the plane touched down. The last two months had been a whirlwind.

The wedding, Mandy and Terry taking over the flat, arranging a transfer to the USA — but that was all behind her.

In the arrivals' hall Roger caught her up in a great bear hug.

"You're here!" he exulted, and held her off, laughing down into her face. "You will be staying this time, I trust?"

"Just you try and get rid of me!" She was laughing with him. "I've come home, haven't I?" ■

by Christine McKerrell.

ALISON SWAN picked up the small parcel and popped across the road to Mrs Dale's. She knew her neighbour would be expecting her, anxious to know how her holiday had gone. It had been Flora Dale who'd persuaded her to book the bus tour in the first place.

"A break's just what you need," she'd said as the summer wore on. "No point sitting around moping — time you got out and enjoyed yourself."

Alison had sighed, knowing Flora was right. Since David had left her for a new life in New Zealand, she had been feeling sorry for herself. It had been over a year now since their divorce, two years since Alison had discovered David had met someone else and was planning to leave her . . .

Flora Dale knew the whole story and had decided it was time Alison left the past behind her. This break was what she needed.

"See," she'd said, pushing a brochure towards her friend, "they even arrange pick-up points in your nearest town."

"But Wales," Alison had protested mildly, "isn't it always raining there?"

"Get away with you!" The older woman had laughed. "Think of all that glorious scenery."

And the scenery *had* been glorious, Alison thought now; the hotel comfortable, the food excellent and the company entertaining. She had really enjoyed herself and was smiling when she found Flora in her kitchen.

"I've just put the kettle on, lass." She smiled. "My, but you look well. You've caught the sun."

Alison nodded as she handed Flora the gift she'd brought back from Wales.

Recipe For Happiness

"Thought you might like something for the collection."

Flora Dale wiped her hands on her apron, smiling in delight.

"I bet I know what this is."

"How many is it now?" Alison asked as her friend delved into the paper bag.

"Never bothered to count." Flora chuckled. "Hundreds probably. Oh, my, isn't that lovely!" She spread the brightly coloured tea towel out on the kitchen table.

"The recipe's for Welsh cake." Alison pointed it out.

"I'll make you some," Flora promised, as she folded the tea towel and put it away. "But, for now, you'll have to make do with one of my treacle scones!"

B ETTY CURRIE was taking a shortcut when she spotted the row of freshly-laundered tea towels bobbing in the wind. A blonde woman was pegging the last of them to the line as she drew level.

"You've a fine collection there," she couldn't resist calling out.

Flora picked up her washing basket and turned to nod at the pleasant-faced woman on the other side of the fence.

"This is only a few of them," she admitted and Betty Currie grinned.

"I'm the same with thimbles."

"Always try to bring one back," Flora told her, "wherever I go. Even if it's only a day trip!"

"Really?" A glint appeared in the other woman's eyes. "I say," she said suddenly, "you wouldn't consider giving a talk to the WI, would you?"

Flora began to shake her head but Betty Currie rushed on.

"I can see it now — 'Travels with tea towels' or possibly 'Tea-towel travels'. What do you think?"

The church hall was gratifyingly full when Flora appeared one evening, armed with her collection of tea towels — and stories. The talk seemed to go down well and Flora had to field several eager questions.

Once it was all over, Betty Currie ushered Flora to the back of the hall, where refreshments were waiting.

"Mrs Dale — you're a natural!" She beamed. "You should consider going on the circuit. Speakers with flair are thin on the ground." She viewed the chattering women with satisfaction. "Best turnout we've had in months.

"I say," she said, turning again to her guest, "you're not a member, are you? Perhaps we could persuade you to join?"

Flora shrugged.

"I'm not too sure — but I do know someone who might be interested . . ."

It had been a popular talk and several WI members pounced eagerly on the recipes on Flora's tea towels. Ella Bainbridge had copied out the Welsh cakes and tried them out the next day.

Ella enjoyed making tea-time treats for the local old folks' home and she was sure these cakes would go down well.

As she did the rounds with tea and cakes a little later, she made sure Major Graham got a hefty slice of her baking. He was such a nice man — so polite and well turned out. It was a shame he had so few visitors.

As George Graham bit into the cake, his eyes misted over. Welsh cake. Of course it wasn't a patch on his dear Glynnis', he thought loyally, but quite delicious all the same.

The trouble was, Glynnis had spoiled him so.

They'd met while he was on a tour of duty in Wales and married within six months. A succession of postings followed — to Germany and Cyprus. His wife had missed Penperis, he knew, though she'd never once complained.

"You can take the lass out of the valleys," he'd tease her gently, "but you can't take the valleys out of the lass!" He caught himself smiling at the memory and sighed deeply. How he missed her!

The smile died on his lips as he thought of his dear wife's plea to make his peace with their son, Alyn. George's eyes clouded — Alyn had been such a disappointment to him.

He could still remember the day Alyn had informed them he'd no intention of taking up the university place that was open to him and even less desire to follow in his father's footsteps.

"I'm not cut out for the Services, Dad," he'd told George. "And I don't need a degree to work the land. Uncle Thomas is willing to have me learn as I go. It's what I want. Surely you understand?"

How could he understand? His son, their only child, a labourer on a run-down farm at the back of beyond. It was unthinkable! He'd had such hopes for him. A great many harsh things were said.

"Go to your blasted farm, then!" George Graham had finally shouted. "But you can expect nothing more from me, boy. You've made your bed and you can lie in it!"

Glynnis had been quietly heartbroken by the rift, though she'd never ceased to hope it might be mended. She and Alyn had kept in touch but, stubborn as he was, George had closed his ears to any mention of his son.

It shamed him now to realise the hurt he must have caused her.

"Everything all right, Major?" Ella Bainbridge's cheery words broke in on George's thoughts.

"What? Oh, fine, Mrs Bainbridge, just fine." He frowned as the woman fussed around, plumping up a cushion or two.

"And did you enjoy the Welsh cake?"

"Splendid, my dear. Splendid. As you can see." George Graham gestured towards the tea plate where only a crumb or two remained.

Ella looked gratified.

"Another piece, perhaps?"

Haytime

HARD they worked in days of yore,
Gathering in the winter store,
All day long, the tractors plied
Up and down the countryside,
Till the yearly crop of hay,
Turned by willing helpers, lay
Spread to dry upon the land,
All the weeds picked out by hand.
Only fragrant clover sweet
Left for hungry stock to eat.

Then, when all the work was done,
Harvest suppers, games and fun,
Tables stacked with country fare;
Young and old released from care,
Dancing to a fiddler's tune
Under an enormous moon.

Those who keep these ancient ways
Still will find, through all their days,
Memories of youthful bliss
Stirred anew by scenes like this.
— *Brenda G. Macrow.*

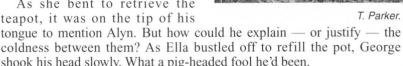

T. Parker.

"Thank you, Mrs Bainbridge." He nodded. "A little bit of home, my dear wife always called it."

"Ah, yes." Ella beamed. "You have friends in that part of the country, don't you?"

As she bent to retrieve the teapot, it was on the tip of his tongue to mention Alyn. But how could he explain — or justify — the coldness between them? As Ella bustled off to refill the pot, George shook his head slowly. What a pig-headed fool he'd been.

He'd been so sure Alyn would come running back, tired of a life on the farm. But generations of his wife's family had farmed that land. It was in his blood. He should be proud of his son.

"Am I too late, my dear?" he spoke into the silence.

"What was that, Major?" As Ella bustled into the room, George Graham came to a decision.

Swaledale, Yorkshire.

"Mrs Bainbridge," he said, his manner as polite as ever, though he couldn't entirely suppress a tremor of excitement, "I seem to be out of writing paper. I wonder —?"

She smiled broadly.

"I'll put it on the shopping list directly, Major. Now, what about stamps?"

*   *   *   *

Alison Swan wheeled the trolley round the spacious lounge, stopping here and there to chat as she handed out tea and biscuits.

"They love a bit of a blether," Betty Currie had confided only weeks before when, thanks to Flora, Alison found herself on the WI rota at the Cedars. "Some of them get no visitors at all, poor souls."

Alison suppressed a smile. On the whole, she'd found the residents of the Cedars anything but "poor souls"! Take the Major, for instance. She glanced over to where the old gentleman sat, deep in conversation with a tall, dark-haired young man.

"Miss Swan, my dear!" George called out as Alison approached. "Come and meet my son."

The younger man had turned, a smile lighting up his pleasant features and Alison found herself smiling back.

"Alyn's come all the way from Wales, my dear. Didn't I hear you say you'd been there recently?"

Alison nodded as she placed two cups and saucers on the small table at the Major's elbow.

"In the summer," she said.

"And did you like it there?" the younger of the two men asked in gentle lilting tones.

"Oh, yes." Alison was enthusiastic. "It's beautiful!"

"Alyn is trying to persuade me to visit this farm of his, Miss Swan," George said happily. "What do you think of that, eh?"

"I can just see you mucking out byres, Major," she teased and Alyn pretended outrage.

"Penperis is arable, I'll have you know! Not that we rely on the land alone these days, mind. It's conservation and farm parks, trail-biking and goodness knows what else now. And what used to be the byres are rather nice self-catering flats. Four star!"

"Well, there's a thing. Four-star byres, no less!" She met Alyn Graham's laughing eyes with a smile.

Later, as Alison put on her coat and got ready to go home, she turned to find Alyn Graham by her side.

"I just wanted to say thanks." He smiled, his dark eyes full of warmth. "For looking after Dad so well."

Alison returned his smile with a shrug.

"Very little to do with me, I'm afraid. The WI run this scheme, you see."

"Oh, yes —" he nodded "— I realise that, but Dad says you've been particularly kind. Listened to him rambling on about the old days." He looked away, suddenly embarrassed. "It's been some time since I got up to visit. I've written to Dad every week but didn't get a single reply. Then, suddenly, out of the blue, this letter came."

Alison nodded — the Major had told her what had happened.

"I'm glad. Your dad's a lovely man."

Alyn smiled wryly.

"Stubborn as a mule, though."

"Now, why," Alison murmured, with the hint of a smile, "do I get the feeling it runs in the family?"

Alyn laughed and Alison smiled widely up at him.

"So, are you driving back to Wales today?" she asked after a moment.

"No, I've booked in at the Royal Hotel for a couple of days. Dad and I have a lot of catching up to do.

"Look," he said suddenly, "perhaps you might join me there tonight for dinner? That is, if you're free. By way of thanks."

Alison shook her head automatically.

"There really is no need —"

"Please," he said, "I'd be glad of the company. Besides —" he smiled mischievously "— didn't I hear you say you'd like to go back to Wales some time? I'm not one to pass up a business opportunity. It'll give me a chance to extol the delights of Penperis!"

A LISON spread the brochures out on Flora Dale's kitchen table. They'd come in the post that morning with a short note from Alyn Graham, saying he hoped to hear from her soon.

"Not a bus trip, this time, Flora," she said. "I know you wouldn't want all that driving about. But I said I would take you to Wales and that's what I'm going to do."

Flora threw her young neighbour a shrewd glance.

"This time last week I'd never even heard of Penperis. Must be some salesman, this Alyn whatsits."

"Alyn Graham. His father's a resident at the Cedars. Mind you, I have a feeling that won't be for much longer."

The Major had confided in her that afternoon that there was a free chalet at the farm Alyn was anxious he would take. He was over the moon.

"By the way, my dear, Alyn says in his letter to be sure to convey his regards. Never married, you know," he'd said, his voice pensive.

"Great disappointment to his dear mother. Still —" he'd cast a covert glance in her direction "— plenty of time for that. Still a young man, by jove."

"What do you think, then?" Alison asked Flora now. "One of the cottages is available in May."

"Very nice. Don't know if I'm up to this trail-biking lark, though," she said dryly.

Alison gave a wry smile.

"I don't think it's compulsory. Shall I write to Alyn and book?"

Flora was pleased to hear the enthusiasm in her voice and saw the faint flush in her cheeks.

When she spoke, Flora had a twinkle in her eyes.

"I could be persuaded — especially as it says here there's a gift shop. It wouldn't be too much to hope," she said, with a chuckle, "that they'll have the odd tea towel for sale now, would it?" ■

POLLY made a cup of tea and wondered yet again if she'd bought the right birthday present for her husband . . . or not. OK, it had to be something special. Well, this was, wasn't it? But, no matter how she tried to reassure herself, she couldn't help wondering. And she had just one more day to make up her mind.

Perhaps she should stick to her original idea? She'd decided weeks ago that he'd like a camcorder and was all ready to go out and buy one.

by
**Rose Mary
Savory.**

Illustration by Melvyn Warren-Smith.

Oh, *why* had she looked in that shop window?

She thought back to that moment, then found her thoughts drifting back to long, long before, when she'd been a young woman . . .

It had been wartime. The siren was sounding and Polly was dashing towards the air-raid shelter.

Once inside, she'd look — as she always did — for the Chapelle family. Their Gallic exuberance made any situation more enjoyable.

Mrs Chapelle, who was originally from the south of France, would be

Love's Precious Gift

bustling around, plump and merry, full of the warmth which always included Polly. Mr Chapelle was British, but with Provençale ancestry, and proud of it.

"The enemy doesn't stand a chance!" Jules, their son, would joke, his twinkling eyes as dark as his mother's.

"My *bébé,*" his mother called him, because he was the youngest of five and all the rest were girls. It didn't matter that Jules was nineteen and working for a firm of builders — his mother still pampered him!

Mr Chapelle would look on, smiling, as his daughters all chatted and laughed with Polly, drawing her into their large and loving family. Her parents were both dead, and she worked in a shop four doors up from the Chapelles' own.

The Chapelle daughters all lived at home and worked locally. Jules, however, was involved in building aerodromes, so sometimes he would be away. Polly's heart would sink as her eyes searched the shelter fruitlessly for him.

Quite often, though, he'd be there and they'd enjoy each other's company, sharing common interests.

It was Jules who'd introduced Polly to photography. Soon, even though she didn't own a camera, she was as enthusiastic as he was.

"They're marvellous," she'd say, when he showed her pictures he'd taken. "Is it terribly difficult?"

"Anyone can do it," Jules declared, spreading his hands wide and laughing with all the warmth of his Mediterranean nature. "When we get the chance, come with me and I'll show you."

POLLY loved those days. They'd get on their bikes, happy to leave the city behind them. They'd share a picnic, lovingly prepared by Mrs Chapelle, and Jules would let Polly try taking some pictures for herself.

She was so touched that he'd let her use his treasured camera.

"It's so peaceful here. It's hard to believe there's a war on," Polly murmured, as they admired wild flowers or stroked quietly grazing horses.

"I know," Jules replied, slipping an arm round her waist as they strolled along. Their friendship was steadily growing into something deeper.

"But one of these days . . ." Jules told Polly one night as they huddled together in the shelter, which was extra full. He smiled, his eyes shining with love.

Warmed by his closeness and feeling safe and secure, Polly smiled, too, as she looked at the photograph in a magazine he was holding.

It was a picture of a very impressive-looking camera, much more complicated than the box Brownie he had at present.

"It's a folding camera that takes roll film or plates. It's very versatile," Jules explained.

"It's wonderful," she said, her tender look letting him know she thought he was, too.

"Once the war's over, we'll soon have cameras and films that can give us colour photos!" Jules declared, grinning broadly.

Once the war's over . . .

As the bombing intensified, the area's residents found themselves in the shelter more and more. The Chapelle family was always a source of optimism and high spirits.

Mr Chapelle had a fine tenor voice and his wife surprised everyone by her ability to play the guitar while Jules knocked out a cheerful tune on his mouth organ. The five girls led the enthusiastic singing that kept everyone's spirits up.

Polly had tears in her eyes when it was her birthday and Mrs Chapelle managed to make her a cake, despite the food shortages.

"You're all so wonderful to me!" she told the whole family as they hugged and kissed her.

But, just as she was about to cut the cake, the siren went and they had to rush to the shelter.

Later on, as they sat in their favourite corner a little apart from the others, Jules gave Polly the best birthday present she could have wished for.

"Oh, Jules . . . I don't know how to thank you!"

She turned the little box camera in her hands and couldn't wait to try it out. Luckily, Jules knew someone who could get a film, but she knew she mustn't waste it.

"It's not new, I'm afraid. But it's in very good condition. And it's the thought that counts, isn't it?"

Looking into his loving eyes, Polly felt her heart sing with joy.

"It was a beautiful thought," she murmured as they kissed.

Polly loved her camera, and taking pictures to show Jules bound them ever more strongly together.

Then, one bright summer's day, he dropped his own bombshell.

"Polly, I'm going to join up."

She looked at his beloved face, his eyes serious and in earnest for once, and knew she couldn't stop him.

"I want to go into the RAF," he continued. "I know I'm doing a useful job and I don't *have* to go, but I feel I want to do more. You do understand, don't you?"

She did, in a way, and was immensely proud of him.

Not long before his departure, he'd held her close, making her feel so safe and secure.

"Pol . . . much as I love you, if you meet someone else, don't let me stand in the way, will you?" Seeing she was about to protest, he went on. "I can't guarantee I'll survive. I want you to be happy. Remember that."

Nonsense, Polly told herself, and him. Of course he'd survive!

The day he went the whole family saw him off, Polly promising to send photos of them all.

"That would mean so much to me," he told her as he kissed her goodbye.

After his training, he became a fighter pilot.

Wish I had time to take pictures from the air, he wrote.

The family drew even closer in their worry for him, but the singsongs in the shelter continued. Polly felt he could almost be there with them.

Malmsmead Ford, Exmoor

HERE stands the farmhouse mentioned in R.D. Blackmore's famous novel, "Lorna Doone". This is a romantic area, with many attractive villages boasting thatched cottages and mediaeval timbered houses.

The moors themselves are home to buzzards, red deer, grouse, sheep and, of course, ponies. Riding is a popular pastime for locals and visitors alike.

MALMSMEAD FORD, EXMOOR: J. CAMPBELL KERR.

The camera he'd given her was very cherished, and she planned to send him pictures to remind him of happiness and home.

Then, the awful day came when she arrived at the Chapelles' house to find Mrs Chapelle in tears and Mr Chapelle looking devastated.

"Missing in action. Presumed dead," he whispered huskily to Polly. "Another pilot saw his plane go down. There was no sign of a parachute. He can't have baled out in time."

Polly's world was shattered. She decided there and then she must step up her voluntary work to help the war effort.

She eased her grief by tirelessly working in the local area, which was still a target for bombs. Every time she saw Jules's family looking a little brighter, her hopes soared that they might have heard from him. But there was nothing.

And then there was Frank.

He was an ex-serviceman who'd been badly injured and would never fight again. Nevertheless, he helped others as much as he could and he had a great sense of humour. Polly was sure his health would improve with time. It didn't take her long to realise they were falling for each other, and she wasn't surprised when he asked her to marry him.

She was torn in two. It was a long time since Jules had disappeared, and they hadn't made any promises, but she still wondered if she should wait until the war was over.

"No, don't wait. Grasp happiness while you can," Mrs Chapelle told her, hugging her to her ample bosom and telling her she'd always be one of the family.

"If you love your Frank then make him happy, the way you did my poor Jules."

Polly realised the family had accepted that he'd never be coming back. And, after so long, her memories of him seemed hazy compared to her vivid happiness with Frank.

They were soon engaged.

POLLY shook herself out of her reverie, her mind made up. She knew that present was the right one now. If she hurried, she'd just be in time before the shop closed.

Two days later, her gift was all wrapped and waiting amid others to be opened.

The family arrived, all greeting each other happily and bringing yet more gifts.

"Glad you like it, Dad!" Each gift was opened in turn, their sons and daughters enjoying their father's obvious delight.

The grandchildren and great-grandchildren jumped around with excitement, wondering what could be in the mysterious and elaborately wrapped present from Grandma. It stood in solitary splendour, the last to be opened.

Silence fell while everyone watched as the wrapping paper was removed.

Polly held her breath, then tingled with joy as she met her husband's eyes.

He turned it over lovingly in his hands, then came to kiss her.

"Wherever did you manage to find it?" he said at last.

"In a bric-à-brac shop, amongst all the junk!" Polly laughed, her eyes sparkling in delight. "Luckily I recognised it for what it was — your heart's desire!"

They kissed again and Polly looked at her husband with tender eyes.

The thick curly hair was almost white now, but the dark eyes still twinkled as much as ever.

She'd thanked the Lord so many times when Jules had come back to her, having passed himself off in occupied France as a native Frenchman. But he'd been unable to get word to England in case he was discovered.

"I baled out late, but made it," he'd told her. "I can thank my slick French tongue and my dark good looks for saving my life!"

He'd helped her get over losing Frank, who'd sadly died of his injuries not long after their engagement.

But Polly felt blessed for her precious moments with Frank, and she was comforted to know that he had been happy.

When Jules had returned, it had been quite a shock for everyone. Especially for Polly, who soon realised that she'd never stopped loving him.

"We might have known it would be a camera!" one of his sisters now said. "You two and your photography!"

Polly smiled at the four of them, all like true sisters to her.

"Ah, but it's not just *any* camera." Jules grinned. "This is something special, from the Forties. It's an antique!"

"I was so worried you mightn't like it," Polly admitted. "The shop owner wanted so little for it, and I kept thinking I ought to be spending more. I'd almost decided on a camcorder . . ."

Jules pulled a face of mock horror.

"Give me this little beauty any time."

He laid the camera down and gently took Polly in his arms again.

"You were wrong about one thing, though. *You* are my heart's desire . . . always have been."

"And it's the thought that counts, as you once told me," Polly answered softly, thinking of the little box camera that was still one of her most treasured possessions.

Just for a moment they were back in the air-raid shelter, young, hopeful and in love. And she knew Jules was remembering, too. ∎

by
Patti Hales.

112

Second Time Around

TIME was running short for Annabel Millen. With only a couple of weeks until the big day, she still hadn't anything to wear. Determined to find the perfect outfit, she and her best friend, Molly, had scoured every bridal shop within a fifty-mile radius.

"I'm either the wrong age — or the wrong shape! It'll just have to be a sensible suit . . ." Annabel moaned over a cup of coffee, in yet another out-of-town precinct.

Her mouth ringed with sugar from her jam doughnut, Molly shook her bright red head.

"No! You wear things like that every day, Annie. Second time around's OK, but second best isn't an option.

"But don't worry, I've been thinking. It mightn't be a bad idea if we look closer to home . . ."

Annabel had been dubious. Theirs was only a very small town. There wasn't a lot of choice. But Molly's suggestion proved sound . . .

Annabel spotted the dress the moment she stepped through the shop door. Her breath caught in the back of her throat as she approached the vision of pure perfection.

Simply cut and classically beautiful, the oyster silk shimmered in the afternoon sunshine streaming through the window. Around the gently scooped neckline, tiny crystals, set in the centre of delicately-embroidered flowers, flashed a myriad of minute rainbows. The scalloped hem, not quite floor-length, allowed a glimpse of ankle.

It was a dress filled with promise. A golden gown. *And* it was within her price range.

But much as she longed to, although she was confident her hands were perfectly clean, Annabel didn't dare reach out and touch. If she did that, she knew there would be no turning back — in spite of her principles . . .

Molly, however, seemed to be harbouring no doubts. She jiggled from one trainer-clad foot to the other and punched the air.

"This is the one! And look — there's even a version for me. In rose, hyacinth or sage. I kind of fancy the hyacinth . . ."

Annabel pretended not to hear.

Remembering her promise to herself, to concentrate on the words of the service rather than worry about how she looked — as she suspected might have been the case at her first wedding when she was so much younger and still a bit silly — she gave the dress a last, lingering glance.

If it had just been pretty, a little less alluring, it would have been fine. But no woman, she told herself, could wear this and not be aware of the idealistic image she was presenting to the world.

Reluctantly, she turned away.

"It's too . . . romantic . . . for a simple ceremony. At my age, I ought to —"

Molly's jaw dropped.

"Good grief, you're not even thirty!" Her green eyes narrowed. "What exactly is it we're searching for, Annie? A smart, all-concealing *shroud*?"

Annabel took her time in answering, struggling to find the right words, while not having the faintest clue what the right words were, since she had, in fact, finally found the dress of her dreams.

"A suit, I suppose," she eventually murmured. "Or maybe a dress and coat. Something practical that I can wear again and not stuff at the back of the wardrobe . . .

"Something simple, which will prove to everyone that I'm taking everything very seriously this time. That there won't be another divorce . . ."

Molly shrugged and began to walk away. But, at the door of the shop, she spun round, clearly exasperated.

"Annie, you've tried hundreds of suits, dozens of dresses, lots and lots of jackets. None of them have been right — and you've never been able to explain why.

"As for proving things to people — I reckon they'll be expecting you to look your absolute best. Glowing! Stunning! Not all apologetic and sackcloth and ashes.

"That dress is perfect. We both know it.

"So what I'm beginning to wonder is . . . are you so ashamed of that blasted divorce that you're having second thoughts about getting married again?"

MOLLY'S words taunted Annabel as she waited for Dan to arrive that evening. They were going for a quick meal and then would call in at the manse for a chat with the minister to finalise arrangements for the service.

"I can hardly wait," Dan had said on the telephone. "It can't come quick enough. I live in fear that you'll change your mind."

Annabel's pulse had quickened. Her heart had swelled with love.

Change her mind? Never!

But that had been before discovering the dress and all its connotations.

If there *were* any doubts lurking deep inside her, she decided now, even the tiniest of niggles, then she'd have to find out what they were and how to deal with them.

Either that, or set Dan free to get on with the rest of his life. But the thought of him holding another woman in his arms, sent a shudder through Annabel.

Of course she wanted to marry him. *And* to look her very best on the big day. It was just that . . .

Elbows on the dressing-table, her chin cupped in her trembling hands, she studied herself in the mirror.

Solemn blue eyes stared back at her.

"What's wrong with me?" Annabel questioned her reflection. "Is Molly right? Am I still ashamed to be the only one in the family to divorce?"

She was still searching for an honest answer when Dan arrived. It didn't take him long to realise that his fiancée had something on her mind.

Annabel was quieter than usual. Pensive. But it was the tiny nerve twitching in her right cheek which really convinced him.

He decided against asking what was worrying her. Experience had taught him that, sooner or later, she would come out with it voluntarily.

And she did. Not in the relaxed surroundings of their favourite restaurant, but afterwards, on the way to the manse.

"About being divorced," Annabel began as they walked hand in hand through the park. "Do you feel guilty about it?"

Dan puffed out his cheeks,

"I suppose I do, in a way. But mostly I feel sad. That I failed the woman I loved — that she failed me. That maybe we didn't take things seriously enough. Maybe we didn't try hard enough."

"That's exactly how I feel," Annabel interrupted. "And that's what Molly doesn't understand — my guilt and my sadness. She seems to think I ought to be celebrating. That it should be like it was the first time.

"I saw this dress today, you see, and it was absolutely gorgeous, but . . ."

They were outside the manse when she finished.

"I'm glad I've got that off my chest, Dan. I'm so relieved you agree with me, darling."

His free hand on the gate, Dan's heart felt heavy. For the very first time he was having doubts of his own. And yet he loved Annabel — had done since he had first set eyes on her.

But a whole future based on guilt and sadness? No! He couldn't imagine that working. If he wasn't able to make Annabel see that, then . . .

Slowly, he turned to face her.

"I *don't* agree with you, Annie. I'm afraid I don't agree at all."

His heart sank as the smile died in her eyes. But, for both their sakes,

A TRIP to the Outer Hebrides is like a journey to a place of enchantment. There are a number of ways to get there, but I love to make a dramatic arrival on the flight from Glasgow which lands on the beach at Barra.

There, you will find scenery awash with colour, particulary in springtime, with crowds of flowers and shimmering lochans.

There's lots of fishing here. Wild Atlantic salmon, though rare, is still available, but most salmon is now commercially farmed.

The Salar Salmon company, at Loch Carnan in South Uist, smoke their salmon using a variety of wood shavings. The result is a dish with a firm, flaky texture, which I can only describe as delicious. It makes a lovely starter or cold main course, but I have tried it in a sort of potato hash which was scrumptious.

Seafood is obviously the dish of the day on any of the islands and shellfish here is particularly abundant and very popular.

Benbecula, situated between North and South Uist, has something of a political edge — a bakery which sells a Scottish Parliament range! Traditional ingredients and recipes make for a great choice of goodies.

Yet, there's still a strong tradition of homebaking here. A cup of tea is usually accompanied by a feast of scones, gingerbread, shortbread or cakes!

There are many local recipes but one which stands out for me is Carrigan Moss Seaweed Pudding. It's served as a cold sweet and is both healthy and delicious.

Further south is the tiny island of Berneray. I would describe it as **the** place to go to really get away from it all.

Prince Charles probably found this out when he visited the island some years ago and stayed with a local crofter there.

He spent some of his time howking potatoes — a worthy pastime indeed, considering the quality of the tatties the fertile island soil throws up.

he knew he had to say his piece.

"I'm with Molly on this one. I know it's going to be a smallish do, but I still want to celebrate *big* time." He smiled gently.

"This is going to be my very last wedding. I want it to be one to remember.

"Corny though it may sound, I can't wait to stand beside my beautiful, fairy-tale bride and put that ring very firmly on her finger. I'm a sucker for organ music and church bells and flowers everywhere.

"I may be several years older and wiser than last time, but I'm still a romantic at heart. I hope there's confetti and that the sun is shining. I want it to be the very best day of our lives."

Dan could see Annabel's lips begin to move. He shook his head. He still hadn't quite finished.

st Beach,
e Of Berneray.

Delicious
Salar Salmon.

Gordon Henderson.

"What I don't want," he continued, "is to dwell on what went wrong before. You seem to feel that divorce is a crime. It isn't. It's just a sad fact of life and I think we've both learned very painful, but valuable, lessons from the experience.

"So, as I see it, there's only one way ahead, and that's to grasp this fresh start like a precious gift. Otherwise . . ."

It was the longest speech Annabel had ever heard him make. As Dan's voice tailed away, tears filled her eyes.

He was right. So very right! Everything suddenly made sense. She had nothing to feel guilty about. Accepting that was like having a huge weight lifted off her shoulders.

She made a mental note to apologise to Molly, too, first thing in the morning. Then she'd invite her to come shopping again!

On tiptoe, she kissed Dan's handsome face.

"I love you so much, but are you sure you want to marry a complete fool?" she queried, her voice wobbly.

Tenderly, he stroked back her hair from her flushed face.

"Not a complete fool. Not even a bit of a fool. Just someone who has put a lot of thought into her life."

Dan grinned as he pushed open the gate.

"Now, about this wonderful dress . . . Do you want me to come with you and give my approval?"

Happiness flowed through Annabel, but she feigned indignation.

"Absolutely not! An experienced romantic like you ought to know full well that it's bad luck for the groom to see the dress before the ceremony . . ."

B Y the time Annabel and Dan reached the altar, most of his wishes had already come true. The confetti and the bells would happen later.

Sunshine streamed through the stained glass; flowers were in abundance, filling the still air with their delicate scents; the organ music soared in triumphant celebration.

And there had been a murmur of approval at the sight of the bride in her oyster silk, a single flower in her upswept dark hair.

"Told you!" Molly muttered gleefully, taking her place at Annabel's side.

"You look stunning, you *both* look stunning," Dan whispered as the minister moved towards them to begin the ceremony.

"Dearly, beloved," he began, "we are gathered together to witness a most unusual ceremony." Deep brown eyes twinkled behind wire-framed glasses. "It's certainly a first for me!

"Eight years ago, in the sight of God and His congregation, I joined Annabel Wright to Daniel Millen in holy matrimony. Today, I am uniting the same Annabel with the same Daniel, only this time their surnames are the same. Very confusing!"

A ripple of laughter echoed round the old building as the elderly man pulled a comical face before continuing.

"Very confusing, very unusual, and very satisfying for all of us who care for this young couple. How our hearts ached when they decided they could no longer live as husband and wife.

"Divorced? Annie and Dan? No, surely not! We didn't want to believe it." He nodded. "And neither did God, who knows a match made in Heaven when He sees one!

"These two didn't divorce in His eyes. They simply took a break from one another. But He does hope they have learned from the experience and are prepared for a whole *new* life together.

"So, Annabel and Daniel, are you now ready to make your vows? Not over again, but fresh, as if it was the very *first* time . . ." ■

W ITH a sigh of relief, Shirley pulled off the dual carriageway and drove through the village, past the health centre, and into the avenue where Tony and his young family lived. She pipped her horn and leaned forward, a smile on her lips, ready to wave to young Nathan.

But there was no Nathan at the living-room window, waiting for her. Probably Kay was busy with the baby, and Nathan was helping.

There was no reply to her tapping on the kitchen door, so she walked around to the front. Then she heard Jody crying, a loud, distressed cry. She was sure she could hear Kay shouting and, further away, Nathan yelling back.

Alarmed, Shirley pressed the bell. The door opened to reveal Kay, obviously very upset, holding a screaming Jody.

Shirley caught a glimpse of her young grandson disappearing swiftly around the top of the stairs.

Hurriedly she dropped her bag and closed the front door.

"Whatever's the matter? What's happened, Kay?" she asked anxiously.

Kay's eyes filled with tears.

"Oh, Shirley, I'm so glad you're here! I don't know what on earth's come over Nathan —"

The tears spilled and Jody, sensing her mother's distress,

Illustration by Gray.

How Does Your Garden Grow?

by Fiona North.

119

increased the volume of her own protest.

"Shall I take her? There, there, it's all right." Shirley placed her screaming granddaughter against her shoulder and began to rock gently to and fro. "Why don't we go and sit down?" she suggested gently to Kay.

Gradually the warm little body began to relax against her.

"Shall I put her down?"

Kay wiped her eyes and nodded.

With loving hands, Shirley placed the sleepy infant in the carry-cot by the settee, and stroked the silky hair until she was sure the baby really was asleep.

"Thanks." Kay sniffed and blew her nose. "I'm sorry."

"Nonsense." Shirley gave her daughter-in-law a hug. She and Kay had always got on well. It was unusual for Kay to get upset.

"I was feeding Jody. Somehow Nathan managed to let himself out of the house, and then got into next door's garden.

"He smashed the glass in one of the cold frames!" She dabbed at her eyes. "I heard the crash and I just knew it was Nathan. I was terrified he'd been hurt."

"So that was what all the shouting was about?"

"It must have sounded awful, but it was such a shock.

"Honestly, all that glass! Whatever is Mr Matthews going to say?" She sighed and leaned wearily against Shirley.

"And Tony . . . he'll think I can't manage. I just wish I knew why Nathan is being so naughty. He *knows* he's not allowed outside without me."

Shirley began unbuttoning her jacket.

"I think a nice cup of tea's in order, don't you? Is the condemned man allowed a drink of juice?"

Kay nodded, the ghost of a smile touching her lips. Shirley was pleased to see her daughter-in-law hadn't quite lost her sense of humour.

SHE carried the juice upstairs and knocked softly on Nathan's bedroom door. He was standing on his little red plastic chair, staring blankly through the window.

"Hello, Nathan. Would you like a drink?"

He climbed down and stood, head down, refusing to meet her eyes.

"I would if I were you," she urged quietly. "It helps when I'm upset."

She sat down on the end of his bed and prepared to wait. After several long, silent moments, Nathan trailed across to her and took the beaker. She saw the abject misery on his grubby, tear-stained little face, and her heart ached for her grandson.

Carefully, she concentrated on smoothing out the cowboy quilt cover.

"When you've finished, do you think you'd like to tell Grandma what happened?"

There was another long silence as he gulped the last of the juice.

"Did Mummy say what I did?"

"Yes, darling." Shirley nodded gravely.

He moved a little closer, his eyes troubled.

"What will Daddy say?"

Carefully Shirley put her arm around him, and this time he didn't pull away.

"I think he'll be a bit annoyed, love. Why did you go into Mr Matthews' garden?"

"I wanted Mummy to play in the sandpit with me, but she was seeing to Jody *again*. She's always seeing to Jody." He sniffed loudly.

"Mummy said you were coming to put some flowers in the garden for her, so I wanted to see if Mr Matthews wanted any.

"But he wasn't there, and I lifted the glass to see what was inside, but it was heavy and I dropped it and it broke." He paused for breath.

"His garden's not much good, Grandma. It's just grass and stones and stuff."

She suppressed a smile.

"Well, at least we can tell Mummy you didn't mean any harm."

"I told her, but she just shouted." Nathan was tearful.

"I expect she was upset, sweetheart. You know what you did was dangerous, don't you?" She stroked his tousled hair away from his face. "Would you like Grandma to go downstairs and tell Mummy what happened, and that you didn't mean to break the glass?"

He nodded slowly.

Kay was dealing with Jody's bottles in the kitchen.

"I feel awful. I mean, he went out on his own; what if he'd wandered the other way, on to the road?" She glanced hurriedly at the kitchen clock.

"I'm supposed to be at the clinic with Jody in quarter of an hour, but what if Mr Matthews comes back? We've only been neighbours a few weeks."

Shirley looked at her daughter-in-law.

"Why don't I get Jody ready while you pop upstairs and have a word with Nathan? Then, if you like, I can take him into the garden with me while you go to the clinic. I'll talk to Mr Matthews."

She smiled, hoping she sounded more confident than she felt. She had never met her son's new neighbour.

* * * *

An hour later she stood in the warm sunshine, and admired her handiwork.

The bronze and orange, yellow and gold would make a lovely show for Kay underneath the kitchen window.

Nathan had been very good, helping her firm in the plants as she put them in, but she had scarcely managed to get a word out of him.

"Nathan, if I carry this box, can you bring the one with the pink snapdragons?"

Croft by Dornie, West Highlands.

T. Parker.

He trailed across the back lawn after her.

"Gran? If the man next door comes back, shall we go in our house?"

"I don't think so. I think we'd better tell him what happened, don't you?" She knelt down. "Put that down there, sweetheart."

"Will you tell him?" His eyes filled with tears and he fisted them away, leaving his cheeks streaked with dirt.

Shirley sat back on her heels and put a hand under his chin.

"I think it would be best if you were very brave and told him yourself. But I'll come with you." She cuddled him to her, a little boy more worried than was good for him, and searched around for a way to help.

"Nathan, how did you get into his garden?" A high wooden fence separated the two properties.

"I'll show you." She had to hurry to catch up with him as he dived into the bushes.

"Nathan!"

His bright little head popped back through the hole in the rotting fence.

"You can get in, too, Gran." He grinned happily. "If you shove that bit, it falls over."

She put a hand on the fence post and the whole section rocked drunkenly.

"No, thank you. I think I'd prefer it if you came back through very carefully."

And then she heard a car pulling into the drive.

"We'll go and have a word with Mr Matthews — get it over with."

She brushed his hair away from his forehead. "Trust me, darling, it's a lot better than worrying about it."

He looked up at her and sniffed.

"You've got a dirty face, Grandma."

Shirley's heart sank a little as she saw the distinguished-looking man in the smart blazer and well-pressed flannels on the other side of the shared driveway. Mr Matthews looked like the tidy, particular type. She remembered Kay telling her that as soon as he had moved in, there had been a skip full of rubbish from the house within days.

"Excuse me, I wonder if we might have a word?"

House Of Dreams

MANY dreams the old croft keeps,
Memories of days not known;
Ghosts of generations sleep
Safe within its walls of stone.

Here the men with crooked spade
Turned the stony soil of yore,
Fertilized with creels of weed
Borne by women from the shore.

Here the children, solemn-eyed,
Often barefoot, walked to school.
Here, upon the mountainside,
Peats were cut for winter fuel.

Life was hard, rewards were few,
Folk had little time to laze,
Yet, sustained by faith, they knew
Sweet content throughout their days.

This old house has seen it all —
Songs and laughter, joy and tears,
Memories that never pall,
Treasured still across the years.

— *Brenda G. Macrow.*

"Of course! Hello, Nathan." He opened his kitchen door. "Please, come in."

Her heart was beating a little too quickly as she took the few steps across the driveway. Nathan was glued to her side.

The kitchen bore out her theory about him. It had probably not been touched since the bungalow was built, but there wasn't a thing out of place.

"How very remiss, do forgive me." He held out his hand. "Jim Matthews. And I'm very pleased to meet you." Hurriedly she rubbed her hands down her skirt. But the only thing to do was plunge in.

"I'm Shirley, Nathan's grandma, and I'm afraid Nathan has had an accident. In your garden." She saw the flash of concern in his face. "Nobody's been hurt, but he's done some damage."

He looked gravely from her to Nathan.

"I see. Would you like to tell me about it, Nathan?"

"I went in your garden and broke your glass. But I didn't mean it. I was looking to see if you had any flowers so my gran could give you some. I'm sorry."

"Well, that doesn't sound too

123

serious." He smiled at them both. "I think the best thing to do is to go and examine the damage, don't you?"

He led them back outside.

"Do be careful of the path, it's not safe.

"Perhaps you'd like to take my arm," he said courteously. "I'm afraid it gets really rickety from here on."

The garden was huge, an overgrown tangle of weeds, ancient shrubs and broken paths. The cold frames were halfway down.

There was a jagged hole in the top panel of the middle one, and slivers of glass glittered in the long grass. On this side of the fence it was easy to see where Nathan had got in.

Jim Matthews followed her glance.

"So that's where he came in. He should never have been able to in the first place. Thank goodness he didn't hurt himself."

"It's a pity about the frame, though."

"I was going to take them out, anyway. Much too dangerous when my grandchildren start visiting and running around.

"So you see, young man, there's no real harm done." He regarded Nathan seriously. "I think it was brave of you to come and own up and say sorry."

Nathan flushed with pleasure, and she heard the hiss as he let out his breath.

"I just wish the rest of it was going to be so simple." Jim Matthews surveyed the wilderness in front of him.

Shirley's practised eye picked out the remains of what must once have been a very pretty garden.

"It's a really good size."

"My daddy says Grandma has green fingers," Nathan put in as Shirley shook her head and smiled.

"In that case, young man, you could do me a favour and persuade Gran to give me some advice." He smiled at Shirley. "I've never had a proper garden before. If this lot gets any worse, you'll need to send out a search party for me!"

"It would be a pleasure to help. And perhaps Nathan could help you to repair the fence?"

He looked at her with understanding and held out a hand which Nathan solemnly shook.

"Good lad." Jim smiled broadly. "Now, why don't we go inside? I'll give you some juice and make your gran a nice cup of tea to seal our bargain."

"It really is very kind of you but we should be getting back. My daughter-in-law will think we've run away from home!"

"That's no problem," he said, easily. "I shall be in all evening. Perhaps later?"

To her surprise, Shirley found herself agreeing.

"That was decent of him," Kay said a little later, relieved. "I mean, Nathan was trespassing." She finished loading the washing-machine and ran a hand through her hair.

"Honestly, I feel I'm just not coping very well at the moment. But with Jody still not sleeping through I'm just so tired all the time. Nathan never seems to be difficult when his daddy's home."

Shirley reached for the tea towel.

"From what Nathan said to me this afternoon, I don't think he is jealous of Jody. He just doesn't understand how much attention she needs. Does Tony really have to be away so much?"

"He's been filling in for sick colleagues, and so on. You know how expensive a new baby is." Kay paused.

"I must admit we'd miss the extra money he's earning, but being on my own so much is really starting to get me down."

Shirley put an arm around her.

"Really, it's something only you and Tony can decide. Why don't you talk to him about it when he rings tonight?" She gave Kay a squeeze.

"But in my experience, children don't really care whether they have expensive things or not. I'll bathe Nathan and get him ready for bed, shall I?

"And then I really must do something with my hair. I'm popping across to see Mr Matthews later on. To discuss his garden," she added firmly. "I felt it was the least I could do."

As she went out of the kitchen to collect Nathan, she was pleased to hear Kay chuckle.

NEXT morning, Shirley was wakened by an excited Nathan bouncing on to her bed fully dressed, ready to help Mr Matthews mend the fence.

She rubbed sleep from her eyes.

"It's only seven-thirty! I'll tell you what, why don't we creep down to the kitchen and make breakfast for Mummy?"

She had heard Jody cry around six o'clock, so she must have gone back to sleep after her early feed. Kay needed to rest.

She could have used a little more sleep herself, she thought, as she made her way downstairs. Jim had proved to be such good company last night that the evening had simply flown.

Like her, he had lost his partner. He'd recently retired from a demanding job.

He was looking forward to sorting out the garden . . .

They had chocolate biscuits with their coffee as he described his old garden.

"It was a pocket handkerchief with a privet hedge and two rose bushes. But I wouldn't have had time for anything larger — teachers really do work, you know.

A Taste Of Harr

VAST expanses of beach set against the backdrop of dramatic hills . . . that is how I remember Harris.

Lewis, its larger neighbour, is flatter, though equally dramatic, with rolling moorlands.

These two islands, though geographically linked, have very separate identities; something which is fiercely maintained by the inhabitants.

But fishing has always been an important part of island life, and these wonderful islands have that much in common.

The best fish and chips I've ever eaten I had one sunny summer's evening in Stornoway. The haddock had been line caught, and I'm sure this had some bearing on the taste . . .

Another Stornoway delicacy is the famous local black pudding. With its unique and delicious flavour, it's in demand the length and breadth of the UK. No island breakfast would be complete without at least one slice, crisply fried, and topped with an egg! And don't forget a tattie scone, popular throughout the Scottish mainland and islands.

Stornoway and Loch Roag on Lewis are the busiest ports in the Western Isles by far. If you happen to be in the right place at the right time, you can witness the arrival of juicy nehrops (Norwegian lobsters) trawled from the Minch, indigo lobsters, velvet, brown and green crabs or rope-cultured mussels.

I often wander down to the harbour at night when I'm in Stornoway. The lights of the returning fishing boats signal a flurry of activity from the men unloading the day's haul, as the sea and noisy seagulls compete aggressively for their share of the catch.

Herring, once the mainstay of the fishing industry here, is still an important part of the summer harvest. Along with its equally tasty partner, mackerel, it's sol fresh, smoked, salted or pickled in brine in the traditional way.

Of course, there's nothing quite like the taste of a supper that you've caught yourself! I once hired a rod and line up at the Laxdale Loch o Harris to catch myself a freshwater supper. The satisfaction of cooking m day's catch on the stony shore in the early evenin is a memory I'll treasure for ever.

"I don't know how you manage. You work full time at the library, don't you?"

She nodded.

"But I find myself wishing I had more time to see the children and do the garden."

He was such a good listener that she found herself telling him her worries about her family.

"I think you gave Kay very good advice." He looked at her carefully. "From the sound of things, you might think about working less hard, too."

"Oddly enough, I have been doing." And she'd told him her plans to

and Lewis

Stornoway.

make enquiries about early retirement. "I thought about it a lot after I talked to Kay. Time to do the things you want is really important, isn't it?"

Kay came down with Jody just as Shirley finished preparing breakfast. She poured tea and nursed the sleepy baby, enjoying the feel of the warm little head against her shoulder, and watched as Nathan chattered away to Mummy about their plans for the day.

The lines of strain from yesterday had eased from Kay's face as she listened happily to her small son.

"Well, it sounds as though you and Grandma are going to be very

127

busy. I'd take your wheelbarrow if I were you; it's bound to come in useful."

Nathan went off to find it while Kay finished her tea.

"I really did appreciate your help yesterday, Shirley."

"Nonsense, I only took Nathan off your hands for an hour."

"A bit more than that! I was telling Tony what you said last night when he phoned, and do you know what I realised? That we were discussing something as important as our children over the *phone.*

"And I realised how much I was beginning to resent it. I feel as though he's a lodger or something, just calling home to get his washing done!

"He's been feeling pretty down in the dumps, too. And he's upset about Nathan. He should have noticed the fence."

At that moment Nathan came bounding back into the room.

"Come on, young man," Shirley said, holding out a hand to him. "You and I have work to do."

Jim was already in the garden, shirt sleeves rolled up.

"I've picked up the glass. I thought Nathan and I would make a start clearing all those weeds so we can see what state the patio is in. And I see he's come prepared. Well done!"

Shirley left them working companionably together and picked her way down to the end of the garden. She and Jim had agreed that it would be nice to rescue as much of the original garden as possible . . .

Two busy hours later, she and Jim were standing beside the almost cleared patio, admiring the pattern of the bricks, when she heard a car pull into the drive.

Nathan sucked up the last of his drink.

"Is that my daddy?"

"I don't think so, sweetheart. He's not due home until late tonight."

"It *sounded* like him."

And a few moments later there was Tony, still wearing his business suit, with Kay beside him, carrying Jody.

Nathan sped across the patio and his daddy caught him mid-leap.

"That's quite a welcome, I must say!" Tony came towards them, bending to kiss his mother. He offered Jim his free hand.

"I believe I have some fences to mend with my son. I do apologise."

Jim shook his head.

"Not at all. As a matter of fact, I seem to remember the fence is a joint responsibility." He smiled. "Nathan and I were just going to start pulling out the rotten wood. Come and see what you think."

Shirley and Kay watched the two men walk down the garden together, Nathan trotting importantly beside his daddy.

"They look as though they're going to be good friends," Shirley said.

"From what I've seen they're not the only ones." Kay smiled.

"What do you mean?" Shirley stared at her.

"Oh, nothing. Just that it'll be nice, keeping things in the family." ∎

LIFE BEGINS AT FORTY

**by
Margaret Brown.**

K ATY shook her head and smiled.

"No, Trish, I think I can honestly say I don't mind. I just wish people wouldn't keep going on about it!

"Being forty is just another number. Thirty-eight, fifty-two — what's the difference?" She shrugged and then glanced up at the kitchen clock.

"Hey, look at the time! If we don't get a move on, our kids'll think we've deserted them."

"I don't want to be," Tricia stated flatly as they climbed into Katy's little car.

"Be what?" Katy was struggling into her seat-belt.

"The big 'four-0', of course. Forty. The beginning of the end. Or the end of the beginning," she said melodramatically as Katy pulled out.

"Do you know you always lose something after you pass forty? Your teeth. Your hair. Your size twelve figure . . . Maybe even your husband."

Katy laughed, shaking her head.

"Honestly, Trish, you do talk rubbish sometimes. Anyway, there's nothing I can do about it and, what's more, I don't care. Now let's talk about something more interesting.

"Thought about holidays yet?"

They were soon at the school, and standing waiting at the gate with several other mums and dads.

As usual, the bottom of Danny's shirt was sticking out his trousers and his tie was undone as he came towards them.

Beth, on the other hand, was as clean and tidy as when Tricia had supervised her as she'd dressed that morning.

"How do you manage that?" Katy whispered to her friend.

"I just threaten to feed her cabbage if she comes home with a hair out of place." Tricia grinned.

"I wouldn't put it past you." Katy giggled.

Danny threw himself at his mother, holding his face up for a kiss.

"Mum! I did a hundred paintings of snails!" he shouted.

Beth tossed her head.

"Oh, no, you didn't!" she yelled. "You did three and they were awful. They looked like hamburgers. But *I* did a beautiful picture of a butterfly — Miss Brand said so. She didn't say *your* snails were good.

"Hello, Mummy."

Tricia caught her daughter and held her tightly.

Just another normal day, Katy thought, smiling, as she dropped them off a little later.

SUPPER over, she settled down to watch her favourite soap while Jack took Danny slowly through the next chapter of "Ben's Holiday at the Seaside".

". . . but Dad's car was old and so they had to —"

"What's old, Daddy?" Katy heard Danny ask.

Jack thought for a moment.

"Well, it's quite difficult to explain," he began. "You see, first you start off young, like you and Eliza's new puppy. And then . . . Well, then you get older. Everything. Everybody." He nodded at Danny but his son was frowning.

"But what *is* old, Daddy?"

Jack sighed gloomily. How on earth do you explain something like ageing to a six-year-old?

He took the coward's way out.

"You'll learn about it when you're older. Now, come on, let's get on with the bit of the story where Dad's car breaks down."

But Danny wasn't to be put off.

"Is tomorrow older, Daddy? Do people break down, too?"

"Katy?" Jack turned towards his wife hopefully but she'd turned the TV up a little and pretended she hadn't heard.

Danny was a very persistent little boy and, as he poured milk on his cornflakes the next morning, he looked at his mother.

"Mummy, are you old?"

It was getting too much, she thought crossly, as she put his toast in front of him. It was a conspiracy and Danny was part of it. She felt herself growing tight-lipped.

"No," she said with a tiny snap in her voice. "And I don't think we want to talk about it any more — OK, dear? Now hurry up, Dad's starting the car."

HER mother was next. At half past eleven, just as Katy was struggling into the kitchen with the shopping, the phone rang. "Katy, dear, I think it's time we talked about your birthday. I mean, it's only five days away and you keep putting me off. But I won't be put off any more."

Katy sighed. She knew not only that tone of voice but also the determination behind it.

"I've told you, Mum," she said, with a bit of the early morning snap still left in her voice, "how I feel about it. Being forty is just being a number. Jack and I are going to Mario's for a meal, as usual. You'll have Danny overnight, won't you?"

"Of course, dear," Angela replied. "But you should be having a party — not just eating out with Jack.

"It's not too late for me to organise a do for you. Won't you let me? Your friends would come, of course, and Nana and Uncle Fred, Auntie Sheila . . . your neighbours. And that nice Tricia. It would just be a little impromptu thing."

Katy stifled a shudder. She knew all about her mother's little impromptu things. Uncle Fred would forget where he was, Auntie Sheila would talk about the war and Nana would complain about Katy's hair.

"Far too young for you, Katy dear."

There it was — age again.

She caught sight of herself in the hall mirror. Her hair swung on the top of her shoulders. That couldn't be too long for forty? Or could it? She suddenly realised her mother was still speaking.

"Are you listening, Katy? What do you think?"

Katy turned away from her reflection.

"You're sweet to think of it, Mum, honestly. But no thanks. And I mean it. No party. We'll drop Danny off at about half past six on Friday — all right?"

"You won't ever have another fortieth, you know," was her mother's rather threatening parting shot.

Later that evening, Katy looked curiously across at Jack as he sat scribbling on a piece of paper. There was something almost furtive about the way he held the paper, as if he was shielding it from her.

She strolled casually across the room, pausing to look over his shoulder. But he was too quick for her and covered the paper with his hand.

"OK, Jack," she said firmly. "Enough. Just what's this all about?

"What are you writing and why are you hiding it? You wouldn't be preparing a surprise party for me, would you? Because, if you are, I'll probably kill you."

He laughed and took his hand away from the paper.

"What a suspicious old thing you are! Oops, I used the 'O' word — sorry. What I'm doing, my darling, is drawing up some plans for that new kitchen you're always on about. Look! I just didn't want you to see it until it's ready."

She gave him a quick kiss on the top of his head, instantly contrite.

"Sorry, dear," she apologised. "But, while we're on the subject, have you booked the table for Friday?"

"Table?" He looked at her, wide-eyed. "Friday?"

"My birthday. We always go to Mario's. You haven't forgotten — you can't have forgotten, Jack!"

He grabbed her arm and pulled her on to his knee, grinning.

"The table's booked for seven-thirty. Oh, Katy, how could I forget? It's your fort —"

She covered his mouth with her hand.

"Don't you dare say it!" She laughed.

A T around half past three on Friday morning, Katy woke suddenly in terrible pain.

"Jack! Jack! Wake up!"

He sat up with a start.

"What's happened? What's wrong?"

She was doubled over, clutching her side.

"Get the doctor — quick!"

Within half an hour, she was sped off to hospital.

The last thing she remembered was seeing Jack's anxious face.

Katy wasn't sure where she was at first when she finally woke up. There was a dull ache in her side and she felt sore all over.

"Katy!" Jack gave her a relieved smile. "You had acute appendicitis, my darling," he whispered, taking her hand and holding it tightly. "You've had an operation — and the surgeon said it all went very well and you'll be home in a day or two." He bent over and kissed her forehead softly. "But please don't ever give me a fright like that again.

"Oh, and happy birthday, Katy dearest."

"Appendicitis?" Katy murmured slowly, her voice sounding miles away. "I can't have had — not without knowing. What time is it? Is it Friday?"

"It's Friday morning — half past eight and you did have it. They said I could have five minutes with you and then you have to rest.

"I'll come back with Danny after school. And I'll cancel that table at Mario's," he added with a smile.

Later, Katy was drifting happily on a huge white cloud when she heard a little voice.

T. Parker.

Gentle Giants

NO machine could match their beauty,
  Bending willingly to toil,
Muscles rippling as the ploughshare
Turns the dark and fertile soil.
Coats of satin, chestnut, bay,
Arching necks and brasses gay.

Men who keep the old traditions,
Though the work is hard and slow,
Find an inner satisfaction
Combine drivers seldom know.
There's companionship and joy
Between a horse, a man or boy.

Stable-scents on frosty mornings,
Swooping gulls 'neath skies of blue,
Harness jingling as their comrades
Plough the furrow straight and true.
Gentle giants, so mild of eye,
Friends of man from days gone by.
— *Brenda G. Macrow.*

"Mummy! Mummy! Are you all right? It's your birthday. I brought you a card and a present."

It was Danny and she reached out an arm to him, wincing slightly.

He deposited a sloppy kiss on her cheek and then looked nervously around the strange room.

"Is this getting old, Mummy?" he asked, his lower lip trembling.

"No, darling," she told him softly. "I've just had to have a small operation, but I'll be home soon. Now, let's see that card and my present."

The painting of the bright red snail surrounded by huge kisses did look a bit like an exploding hamburger. She smiled as she opened the tiny bottle he'd carefully wrapped and dabbed some of the perfume behind his ears.

"Just wait until Beth smells that," she said. "She'll probably want to marry you there and then."

"Yuk!" he exclaimed, rubbing his ears vigorously.

She was tired by the time Jack and Danny waved goodbye from the end of the ward and sank back against her pillows.

It was after dinner time when Sister Harrow came bustling in.

"Just as well we're not full," she remarked, fussing over Katy's pillows. "So you have a special dispensation."

"Dispensation?"

Sister Harrow gave a slightly disapproving tut.

"Half an hour, I told them. Half an hour and then out," she said before sweeping out.

Jack and Danny were first, followed by Angela and then Uncle Jack, Nana and Aunt Sheila.

Then came Jean and Cameron from next door, Jim and Mary, their oldest friends, and Peter, her brother. They all carried brightly-wrapped parcels and gathered around the bed, smiling.

Then, the door suddenly flew open with a flourish.

Tricia marched in, carrying a large cake.

They were in the middle of singing "Happy Birthday" when Sister Harrow bustled in, wearing the look of an avenging angel.

"Now I must insist — everybody out, please. Mrs Armour must get her rest — birthday or no birthday."

"I won't marry Beth," Danny told Katy as he slithered off her bed. "Ever!"

"I love you, sweetheart," Jack said softly. "And when you come home, we must start planning your forty-first birthday party."

Katy squeezed his hand.

"If I had the strength, Jack Armour, I would probably kill you here and now."

The last kiss was from Tricia.

"See?" she whispered. "I told you you would lose something when you got to forty — and you did!" ∎

$\mathcal{B}aby$ $\mathcal{L}ove$

Illustration by Mark Viney.

"YES, Baby can smile." Deb leaned over the crib and flicked the Cheshire Cat mobile. It swung gently, casting shadows over her daughter's face.

"We'll have to stop calling you Baby, sweetheart," Deb went on. "You're nearly big enough for a real name, aren't you?"

The baby blew a string of bubbles and waved her tiny fist. Little lovey-dovey, Deb thought to herself, then looked round, feeling a bit foolish.

Before Baby had arrived, she and Terry had agreed: no twee talk, no spoiling. She grinned to herself. As if. Terry was worse than she was!

She doubted if mother-in-law would be, though.

She felt depressed at the thought, but the visit couldn't be put off. Baby was six weeks old and enough hints had been dropped by letter and phone.

Deb crossed to the window and lifted the curtain. It promptly slid off its rings and fell to the floor. She stared down. Crumpled Tom and Jerry.

She'd loved the cartoon characters as a small child, but when she'd bought the material, Terry had asked if it was quite the thing for a new baby's room.

"They're a bit . . . well, violent, really," he'd said. "What about some jolly nursery animals?"

"I had abstract art," Deb had said. "Really cool squares and oblongs." Her father had been a keen amateur painter.

by Valerie Edwards.

135

"I had Sooty and Sweep."

"You *would*," she'd said scornfully. "Your mother would never have anything controversial."

Now, she picked up the curtain and folded it over her arm. There was a streak of dirt across the hem.

It wasn't fair, she told herself. Everything she touched either fell to pieces or covered itself in grime. And, of course, it had become worse since Baby arrived.

There was never enough *time*. Well, there was, but she preferred to spend it with her daughter.

At least I've given up reading, she thought virtuously — while I'm cooking, anyway.

Ever since they'd got married, she'd stirred saucepans with one hand whilst devouring her favourite authors with the other. She thought she'd perfected the art until the day she'd set fire to the oven cloth and hadn't noticed.

Terry had come into the kitchen just in time.

"I thought I could smell the dinner burning," was all he'd said.

She hadn't done it again. It had been too scary. Too dangerous.

She went downstairs and stuffed Tom and Jerry into the washing machine. A pair of socks fell out, followed by a teacloth. She pushed them back and firmly closed the door.

She'd do the load tomorrow. Definitely. Get up very, very early . . .

"The whole house is a mess," she said aloud, feeling quite suddenly that, if she wasn't careful, she could quite easily burst into tears.

Self-pity, she scolded. Pull yourself together. Make a start — wash your hair.

Determinedly, she turned on the tap, opened the cupboard and found the shampoo. The bottle was empty.

If she put some warm water in, perhaps there would be enough . . .

Towelling her hair dry afterwards, she told herself she was lucky — people were always saying so — that she had natural curls.

Only you could never do anything sophisticated with them, her mother-in-law had said from underneath her own immaculately permed grey hair.

"Of course, it's different with men," she'd gone on.

They'd been sitting in the spotless lounge. Terry and his two older brothers had all disappeared to the pub for a pre-lunch pint.

Deb would have liked to have gone, too, but in this house women knew their place. And that definitely wasn't in the Horse and Groom.

Sometimes Deb had wondered what their late father (their mother had brought them up — heroically — on her own for the last ten years) had really been like, but Terry had insisted he'd been treated exactly like her sons.

With due reverence, Deb had added. Terry had given her a quizzical look, but hadn't answered.

Baby Love

"How — different?" she'd countered.

"It just is," her mother-in-law had said indulgently. "All my boys had lovely wavy hair."

"Not now," Deb had pointed out remorselessly.

"Well, one expects that, as they get a little older. I'll just check the roast, dear. It's lamb — Terry's favourite."

It would be, Deb had said silently to her retreating back. And it'll be just you and me doing the washing up while the men watch telly — as usual.

Why does she always make me feel so inept, she thought now. I can never live up to her idea of perfection. Goodness knows how much she'll disapprove of me as a mother.

She picked up Terry's discarded newspaper and an empty yoghurt pot. He did *try* to help, although, since their marriage, the concept of shared housework and parenting hadn't been that easy to get across. It had been his mother's proud boast that she didn't believe in equality — men needed to be looked after.

The last time her mother-in-law had come, she'd been the one to find the broken digestive biscuit under the cushion and the half-eaten Pot Noodle on the corner of the window-sill.

And she'd even caught her surreptitiously cleaning the brass door knocker at seven-thirty in the morning!

When Terry came home, she was sitting despondently in the armchair with Baby on her knee. Baby looked beautiful in blue.

That would cause comment, no doubt.

"Any minute now," Deb told Terry on a sigh.

"Mum's not so bad," he murmured. "She's not perfect you know."

The trouble was, Deb thought, she is! I know it — and she knows it.

They heard the taxi drive up, and then pull away. Terry went to answer the door and as Deb half-turned, the baby was sick all over her shoulder. She felt ready to weep.

Then her mother-in-law was in the room, almost rushing towards her. And then she stopped. No wonder, Deb thought dully. What a mess we both look.

And then she saw the other woman's expression. She was absolutely entranced. There was no other word for it. She held out her arms.

"Oh, Deb," she almost whispered. "You've managed to do the one thing I've wanted to do all my life — have a lovely little girl of my own."

Her eyes were full of tears as she held her granddaughter close.

And it was at that very moment that Deb knew, without doubt, that a miracle had happened.

From now on they were to be equals. Somehow, she had to cement the new relationship. She did it in the only way she knew how.

"We're going to call her Mhari," she said. "After you, Mum."

And the gratitude and admiration on her mother-in-law's face made her feel at last — at last — ten feet tall. ■

Just Good Pals

VICTORIA had just got back from the office when Aunt Ev phoned to tell her the bad news.

"I've taken a bit of a tumble, dear," she explained in her usual matter-of-fact-way.

"Doctor Jackson says it's only a badly bruised ankle. He strapped it up for me and I'm using one of Dan's old walking sticks to get around.

"But it couldn't have happened at a worse time. I promised the children I'd be at the fête tomorrow. If I don't turn up, they'll feel responsible."

"Well, let's face it, two of them are," Victoria reminded her gently.

by Sheila Aird.

Aunt Evelyn, her godmother, was now her only living relative — and an increasing source of concern. On the outside, she looked a sensible sixty-eight-year-old woman. Inside, she was the same age as the children she escorted across the busy road which cut through the village of Kilmore.

The culprits in question, Jamie and Hannah, had fought each other for the honour of holding Aunt Ev's hand while she, in her role as lollipop lady, stood at the edge of the pavement waiting for the traffic to ease. In the confusion, the lollipop had slipped from her grasp and had become tangled up in three pairs of legs.

"Luckily, Jamie and Hannah are none the worse," Aunt Evelyn went on. "The only problem is Charlie."

Victoria smothered a sinking feeling.

"What about Charlie?"

"I've entered him for the 'best-behaved dog' competition at the fête," Aunt Evelyn confessed and Victoria suppressed a chuckle.

"We've been practising hard for weeks and he's ever so good. It would be a pity if he couldn't compete, though. I don't suppose you . . .?"

Victoria groaned. She'd do anything for her aunt — anything, as long as it didn't involve Charlie. For some reason, the collie — who Aunt Ev had acquired from a friend six months ago — had taken an instant dislike to her and bared his teeth at every opportunity.

"Of course, he'll be competing against some very good dogs," her aunt mused. "Ned Brander's Toby, for a start."

Victoria's heart tumbled.

"Is Ned home for the weekend?"

"Not only for the weekend. He's back for good. His father is retiring soon, so Ned will be taking over the practice. Didn't you know?"

Ned Brander had lived and worked in the city for five years, and he'd been engaged to a sophisticated business consultant for the past six months. His return to Kilmore to take over his father's law practice was the last thing Victoria would have expected.

"What about Louise?" she asked. "I thought she'd made it clear she wasn't interested in living in the country."

"Oh, that's all over," Aunt Evelyn said cheerfully.

Victoria considered this information for a moment.

"I'll drive down this evening," she said quietly. "Just don't expect miracles where the dog competition is concerned."

AFTER she'd rung off, Victoria's thoughts were in a muddle. Why hadn't Ned told her Louise had broken off their engagement? When they were children, growing up in Kilmore, she and Ned had been best friends, as close as any two people could be.

They'd always done everything together. They'd cycled the lanes round the village, played tennis and badminton and, in between studying for exams, they'd been enthusiastic members of the youth club.

When they both went to different universities — in her case to St Andrews to study accountancy, in his to Glasgow to do law — they'd kept in touch by phone. And they'd always met up during vacations.

Their special friendship had survived even after she settled in Edinburgh and Ned went to work in London.

Melrose Abbey, Roxburghshire

FOUNDED by Cistercian monks in 1136, Melrose Abbey has survived a turbulent history. It has seen many a battle but now lies quietly, within its walls, the resting place of the heart of Robert Bruce.

Many visitors come to admire the fine stonework, which includes many carvings and graceful arches, and also to learn about the history which has shaped the Abbey.

MELROSE ABBEY,
ROXBURGHSHIRE:
J. CAMPBELL KERR.

141

Every Christmas and Easter they'd both head for Kilmore like a pair of homing pigeons. They'd spend the holiday talking non-stop — as friends do.

No matter how long they were apart, they could pick up where they'd left off. Their friendship was special.

So when Ned fell in love with Louise, Victoria had been the first to know.

They were sitting at a corner table in the local café when Ned told her about the girl of his dreams.

"She's wonderful, Vic. Absolutely perfect. You'll adore her."

Here we go again, Victoria thought. Ned had been falling in and out of love regularly since he was sixteen. Usually she'd been there to pick up the pieces when yet another "most wonderful girl in the world" had let him down.

Now, she would've teased him about his choice of phrase if something in his expression hadn't stopped her.

"How long have you known Louise?" she said, gazing at him over the rim of her cup. "I mean, just three weeks ago you were a twenty-nine-year-old bachelor, footloose and fancy free."

"Actually we met just eighteen days ago — at a business lunch."

His smile made her heart beat faster. She nodded, imagining the scene.

"Love at first sight, then?" she asked gently.

"Yes!" His enthusiasm was touching. "Oh, Vic, that's exactly how it happened. I knew you would understand."

For a moment she'd forgotten what was happening. She'd shared his joy.

"I'm going to ask Louise to marry me."

"What?" Victoria felt as if she'd been hit by a thunderbolt. "Marriage is a big step, Ned."

"But a logical one."

"I suppose so. But are you sure you're ready?"

"I love her," Ned said simply.

Victoria didn't know what to say. She simply stared at him.

Suddenly she realised nothing would ever be the same again. And, equally suddenly, she also knew Ned had stopped being her "best friend". He was more than that now. She was in love with him.

"So, when do I get to meet her?" She forced out the words.

A few weeks later, Ned phoned to ask her to make a special journey to Kilmore. Louise had agreed to come north for the weekend.

The sad thing was Victoria knew the truth the moment Louise walked into the room, clutching Ned's arm possessively. She was so obviously an "up-town girl" there was no way she'd approve of his plans to take over his father's law practice. She would hurt him like all the others . . .

Now, six months on, Ned had realised falling in love at first sight across a crowded room was not a good idea. But he hadn't mentioned anything about his broken engagement to her. Obviously he could cope on his own.

So what happened to that special something we had, Victoria wondered, feeling hurt and confused.

It was almost eight o'clock that evening when she turned into Aunt Evelyn's driveway. Letting herself into the house, she went straight through into the cosy kitchen. Her aunt was watching her portable television, her foot up on a stool.

"It's wonderful to see you, love," Auntie Ev said after they'd hugged and she'd assured Victoria that her ankle was healing nicely. "Hope I haven't spoiled your weekend."

"You haven't. Honestly. It's ages since I've been here for the fête. I'm looking forward to it."

"Wonderful. The chicken casserole's nearly ready. Will you dish up?"

Victoria took a pair of oven gloves from the kitchen drawer. "So, where's Charlie?"

As if he'd heard his name, Charlie slid round the kitchen door and tiptoed across to sit at his mistress's feet.

He stared up at Victoria. She stared back at him.

This time there was no ferocious barking, no bad-tempered growls. For almost ten seconds she gazed into Charlie's intelligent brown eyes, then the dog looked away.

"I've told him you'll be in charge tomorrow and he's happy with that," Auntie Ev said. "And he's not jealous any more."

"So, that was it." Victoria bent down to Charlie's level. "Why were you jealous? Daft dog. There was no need to be."

Charlie yawned lazily, eased himself into a more comfortable position and smiled. At least Victoria could have sworn it was a smile.

"So, do we have a truce?" She put out her hand to tickle Charlie under his chin and felt the dog's rough tongue on her fingers.

"I assume that means 'yes'. D'you think we could win the competition for Auntie Ev tomorrow?"

The dog opened his mouth and grinned hugely. He obviously understood every word. Winning was going to be a doddle . . .

WE'LL need to find somewhere to sit close to the judging ring," Auntie Evelyn said next morning as Victoria parked the car. "There are some hay bales outside the tea tent." Victoria was looking around anxiously. "Can you walk that far?"

"Of course. But I'll take my time. You go on by yourself."

Victoria was walking across the crowded field towards the tents and stalls when Charlie pulled on the lead. A Dalmatian of huge proportions was dragging a tall, dark-haired young man towards them.

Victoria forced herself to stay calm.

"Hello, Ned. I see Toby's in good form."

"As usual." Ned smiled, looking rather embarrassed. "Good to see you, Vic. I was hoping you'd be here this weekend."

T HERE'S something very special about Orkney which I can't quite put into words. Its rolling gold and green landscape and startling cliffs sit strangely beneath an immense sky. Nothing about the island is predictable — you can never be sure what you're going to find around the corner!

A Taste O

© Original Orkney Hamper Co.

If you're a cheese lover, then Orkney is the place to be. A local cheesemaker was once told that the reason his cheese tasted so good was because his cows have such bonnie views! This may also explain the island's delicious beef, too.

There's something unique in almost every aspect of life on Orkney. The North Ronaldsay sheep, for instance, eat only seaweed! I noticed that they are kept on the shore with drystone dykes. Their unusual diet produces a very distinctive mutton.

If your visit happens to coincide with the arrival of a new potato crop, you should consider yourself lucky! It's one of the culinary events of the year. The writer George Mackay-Brown famously wrote of the Orcadian potato: "All praise to the Orkney tattie. You can taste the dark earth-strength in it; the sun; the sweetness of rain."

I had never come across bere until my first visit to Orkney. It's an

He leaned forward to kiss her cheek, but she side-stepped the gesture by tugging at Charlie's lead.

Charlie moved obediently to heel and stared at Toby, who leaped forward, dragging Ned with him.

Obviously puzzled by Victoria's behaviour, Ned hauled the dog back to his side.

"He's impossible today."

Victoria didn't comment.

"Look, I need to talk to you," he said. "Let's go for a walk by the river."

"If you want to tell me that Louise broke off your engagement, I already know." She bit her lip.

"I'm sorry it didn't work out. Now, if you'll excuse me, I have to check Charlie's entry for the competition."

Ned didn't attempt to follow her as she strode across the field to the official caravan.

Victoria spent the next hour or so wandering round the various stalls. She bought a bunch of dried flowers for Auntie Ev and a pretty photograph frame for herself.

144

Orkney

Ring of Brodgar.

ancient variety of barley, dating back to the Stone Age. Try a bere bannock. It's an acquired taste for some. But, for others — such as myself — it's love at first nibble!

I have to confess that my favourite Orkney dish is ice-cream. It's what I call *real* ice-cream, made the old-fashioned way with full dairy cream.

And what better way to wash down your Orcadian dinner than with a glass of golden ale from the brewery at Quoloo? I have it on good authority that the local water is just right for making the beer which, I've noticed, is steadily growing in popularity all over the country. And no wonder!

If a stay in Orkney whets your appetite for local foods, it's easy to take home a taste of the islands. The Original Orkney Hamper Company send Orkney fare the world over. So now there's no excuse not to try local cheese, sweets, baking, beers, whisky, fish, oatcakes . . .

The second-hand bookstall caught her interest and she browsed for ages — much to Charlie's disgust — before splashing out on a book of poems.

Ned, too, was exploring the fête. Victoria followed his progress round the field, watching him laughing and talking with old friends.

Once or twice she saw him on his own. He looked so sad she wanted to rush over and tell him to cheer up, that being jilted by Louise didn't mean it was the end of the world.

Then she remembered he hadn't even told her about the break-up. That made her feel hurt and annoyed again.

LATER, she and Charlie lined up in the ring with the other competitors for the Best-Behaved Dog competition.

When it came to his turn, Charlie was magnificent. Victoria felt quite smug.

Then, as they left the arena, they passed Ned, who was talking to an old schoolfriend. Toby was sitting quietly at his feet. But not for long. The minute he saw Charlie, he jumped forward, tweaking his lead out of Ned's hand.

To his credit, Charlie resisted the impulse — for a moment or two. Then the temptation proved too much. He gave his head an expert twist and slipped his collar and raced away after Toby.

Ned was suddenly by her side.

"Come on. We've got to catch them before they really get into trouble," he hissed.

He grabbed her hand and they began to run after the dogs. The crowds parted to allow them through and, seconds later, they'd left the field and were stumbling down a path which led to the river.

"Wait!" Victoria was breathless. "Let me catch my breath."

It was quiet now. She leaned against a tree, but Ned moved around restlessly. Suddenly he came and stood in front of her.

"What's wrong, Victoria?"

She stared at him.

"*You* want to know what's wrong? *You're* the one who spoiled everything."

"What are you talking about?"

"I thought we were friends —" Her voice cracked. "But you didn't even tell me Louise had broken off your engagement."

"So, that's it." He looked as if he was debating with himself what to say next. "Why would I tell you Louise had broken off the engagement?"

"Everybody else knew!"

"Everybody else *assumes* Louise ditched me," he shot back. "But she didn't. In fact, I wanted you to be the first to know *I* broke it off. I told her I couldn't go through with the wedding."

"Why?"

Ned moved forward to look down at her.

"Can't you guess?"

Victoria's heart almost stopped as she gazed into his eyes.

"I don't want to be your best friend any more, Victoria. I should have realised ages ago how I really feel about you. How do you feel about me?"

She slipped her arms round his neck and pulled him towards her.

"Do I have to spell it out?"

"I love you, Victoria." He made a face. "I think I always have."

He bent to kiss her but, before their lips met, the sound of heavy breathing made them both look round.

Charlie and Toby were moving sedately up the path, the picture of two well-behaved dogs. They glanced at each other when they saw Victoria and Ned.

Then, as if they knew they were intruding, they simply kept on walking towards the field where the prize for the best-behaved dog was being presented to a sweet little King Charles spaniel.

Victoria looked up at Ned.

"Where were we?" he murmured as he took her in his arms. ■

Illustration by Mike Heslop.

Crossed Wires

by Coral Newell Leend.

"HAVE I been put through to a Miss Anne Jones?" a deep male voice asked over the phone.

"That's right, sir!" Anne said brightly.

"Then can you help me?"

It was the most attractive voice ever, Anne decided. She wanted to say something silly, like, "Yes, please!" but refrained.

"I hope so, sir," she told him quickly.

"I've received the most extraordinary letter from you. It says I owe you three hundred and forty-two pounds!" His tone had risen and he sounded suddenly irate — like the majority of the calls they received. "It's impossible."

Anne sighed. For once, she'd been hoping for something different. Just one spark of pleasure in her difficult, mostly unappreciated, job. But no. It appeared that this caller was going to be no different from any of the others.

"If you'll just give me your name and our reference number, I'm sure we'll soon sort this out."

"My name is Jason Whitefield, and your reference number is WS twenty-four W."

Anne hesitated with a puzzled frown, hands poised over her keyboard.

"I think you've made a mistake, sir. That isn't one of our numbers."

"Look, I have the form in front of me and it states clearly WS twenty-four W," he barked crossly.

"I'm sorry, sir, but that's certainly not one of our numbers," Anne repeated calmly.

"Heck! Why is it impossible to get sense from the Civil Service?"

"Let's start again," he began, enunciating slowly. "My name is —"

"Jason Whitefield!" Anne broke in sharply. "I took a note of your name. There's obviously something amiss here. Perhaps you could give me your address?"

She keyed in his name and address.

"One moment, please." His name came up on her computer screen but with a different address. "Your middle name is Mark?"

"Yes!" he snapped.

"I have a Jason Mark Whitefield, but he lives at number two, Somerset Pla —"

"That's when I was a student," he interrupted, groaning again. "This is ridiculous."

"Hang on!" Anne said, as a thought struck her. "Can you tell me the sender's name and address?"

"Miss Anne Jones, Filburgh Council Tax Office —"

Anne chuckled.

"This isn't the Council Tax Office — you've been put through to the Housing Department.

"Obviously they have someone called Anne Jones, too. It's not exactly uncommon. I'll transfer your call."

The incident kept her amused for the rest of the morning, her thoughts wandering back to that gorgeous voice.

"I wonder what he's like?" she muttered.

"That's a bad sign," her friend, Penny, said with a grin.

"Isn't it?" Anne agreed, and told Penny all about it. "I'm off for an early lunch now. See you later."

Crossed Wires

Y OU missed him." Penny pounced on Anne when she returned to the office.

"Who?" Anne asked.

"Mr Whitefield, the one with the gorgeous voice you were going on about earlier. And he's really good-looking. He asked for you."

"Did you tell him I'd be back?"

"He couldn't wait, he was going to the Council Tax Office." Penny laughed. "He said there'd been a mix up when he moved house and they've charged him twice!"

Anne giggled.

"That's why he sounded so cross!"

Later that afternoon, a broad-shouldered, tall man came through the door, clutching a bunch of flowers. His eyes flashed straight to the name on Anne's desk, then he took his place in the queue in front of her position, patiently waiting his turn. At last, he dropped onto the chair in front of her, regarding her with some approval.

"Miss Anne Jones?"

She knew his voice immediately.

"That's right. Can I help you?"

"I'm sure you can . . . I hope so anyway. I'm . . ."

"Let me guess. Jason Whitefield?" She grinned. "What can I do for you, Mr Whitefield?"

For a moment, he just sat staring at her. Anne flushed slightly, becoming aware of the waiting queue, all watching curiously. He noticed, too, and leaned forward over the desk towards her.

"I'd like to make amends. Can I take you out to dinner this evening?" he whispered, just loud enough for her to hear. "Please."

"I think I can manage that," she said briskly, in a formal tone. "One minute, sir. I'll need some details."

She grabbed a form and jotted across it, *Where? What time?* Before passing it back to him.

"Will you fill in this form, please?" she said with a smile.

La Brazzièr. I'll pick you up at eight. What's your address? He passed it back.

"One more point, sir." She added her address and phone number. "I think you have all the information you require. You can take the form with you."

"Thanks a lot. You've been very helpful, Miss Jones."

"That's what we're here for." She laughed as his eyes widened in mock astonishment. He got up, flashing a dancing glance down at the flowers, which he left on her desk.

"Next, please," she called, watching him disappear through the door.

"What a shame. That young man's left his flowers," the next woman said as she sat down. "I expect he'll come back."

"I expect he will," Anne agreed with a smile. ■

Illustration by David Young

150

A PRESENT FOR JAKE

by Janet Bond.

K AREN pushed her way through the Saturday morning shoppers in the toy department. Exhausted, head pounding in time to the Christmas muzak, she stared miserably at the Action Man display.

At these prices, the money Steve had given her wouldn't go far.

Steve. She could see him now, his clean-cut face etched with worry as he checked his wallet early this morning.

"Here. You'd better get that present for Jake while you're out today," he said, pushing a single banknote across the kitchen table.

Ten pounds!

"You must be joking. That won't be nearly enough." She cocked her head, listening for sounds of movement from above. But their small son was still asleep.

"It won't even pay for the Action Man he's set his heart on, let alone all the gear to go with it. Haven't you any idea how much these things cost?"

Steve frowned.

"More than we can afford at the moment, I'm afraid." He reached across the table and squeezed her hand gently.

"You'll have to get something else, then. How about a giant colouring book and a new set of pens?"

"Oh, come on. Nearly everyone at playgroup has an Action Man and he naturally wants the same."

Steve's frown was still there.

"If you're short of ready cash, I'll put it on the credit card," she offered.

"I'm sorry, love." Steve shook his head. "We're already overdrawn, and I'm determined not to run up any more debts. Until the housing market picks up, we'll have to watch every penny."

"But it's Christmas," she urged. "And Jake doesn't understand about there being a shortage of work."

"He'll have to learn, then. I'll do my best to explain while I'm looking after him today." Steve rubbed his hand over his face.

It was all so unfair. Just as Steve had got somewhere with his builder's business and they were getting used to a comfortable way of living, a couple of main contractors had gone bust.

Suddenly, they were back to square one.

"If only I was working . . ." she began.

"Don't even think of it," Steve cut in. "We agreed that you should stay at home until Jake starts proper school. Besides, I was rather hoping that by then . . ." His words trailed off.

Mechanically, Karen shrugged on her coat.

"I'd better go before the Saturday rush begins. After all, that was the whole point of getting up early."

"Bye," Steve murmured, returning her kiss. He followed her to the front door.

"Don't look so worried, love. I'm sure you'll rise to the challenge."

TURNING away from the large display, she studied the price tag on a copy of the doll.

"We can easily afford to buy one of these," she told herself. "It could be an option."

But, deep down, she knew that, even at his tender age, Jake could tell the difference.

She imagined him on Christmas morning, tearing the wrapping paper from a poorly dressed, cheap imitation, and sighed.

Oh, well. With any luck, cash might be a bit more plentiful by his birthday. Meanwhile, she would have to do as Steve had suggested and settle for something quite different. But what?

"Cheer up. It may never happen."

Recognising the familiar Scottish voice of her neighbour, Karen turned.

"Hello, Mrs Macgregor! How are you?"

"I'm fine, my dear. But you look down in the dumps. That's not right

The Three Sisters Of Glencoe

GLENCOE can be a haunting spot in misty weather and translates from Gaelic as Glen Of Weeping. It was here that the famous massacre of 1692 took place, when the Campbells turned on their hosts, the MacDonalds.

Towering over all, and the highest hill in Argyll, is Bidean nam Bian. The three sisters — Beinn Fhada, Gearr Aonach and Aonach Dubh — all lead up to this lofty top and make a dramatic sight summer or winter. Look carefully on Aonach Dubh to see Ossian's Cave, reached only by a rock climb. Ossian was a Gaelic poet reputed to have been born in Glencoe.

THE THREE SISTERS OF GLENCOE: J. CAMPBELL KERR.

for this time of year!" The older woman patted Karen's arm fondly.

"Come on, let me treat you to a coffee. The café's right here on this floor."

Refusing to take no for an answer, she led the way.

"With Christmas so near, you must be awfully busy." Eliza Macgregor stirred sugar into her cup. "I remember how it was when my lad was small."

She smiled, and a faraway look came into her eyes.

"Hunting for things to put in his stocking. Racing around the shops, only to find them sold out of the one toy he most wanted! Either that, or it was too expensive."

"I can relate to that," Karen admitted, looking up. "Steve's been struggling for work again recently . . ."

"I'm so sorry, my dear, I had no idea . . ." Eliza's voice faltered. "I didn't mean to embarrass you."

"I know." Karen smiled at her. "Actually, it's a relief being able to tell someone. We don't want to worry our parents — they've helped us enough already." She threw back her head.

"Hopefully, business will pick up again in the New Year. But, for now, the thing that hurts most is having to stint on Jake's presents . . ."

Talking it over with Eliza seemed to help.

"What do you think?" she asked eventually. "Given the choice, would he prefer to wait until we can afford a genuine Action Man?"

"Would you in his place?"

"Yes." Karen didn't hesitate.

They drained their cups, gathered up their shopping and left together. They were caught up at once in the crowds milling around the jigsaw puzzles and board games.

"Jake's too young for most of these anyway," Karen remarked, moving on to the books. The two women stopped to browse.

"Now there's a bargain!" Karen snatched up a book with a reduced sticker on its cover.

"Look, a Rupert book. Jake loves these stories. I'm tempted to buy it. Not that it's very exciting, compared to an Action Man, is it?"

"Oh, I don't know." Eliza smiled. "My boy always treasured his annuals. Come to think of it, I remember making the little bear for him, many years ago.

"I don't know what happened to it, but I do believe I may still have the knitting pattern at home!" Her wrinkled face broke into a grin.

"If you like, I'll look it out for you."

"Would you?" Karen felt better. A Rupert book, complete with bear, would be just up Jake's street — but . . .

"There's only one snag. I can't knit!"

"I can teach you," Eliza volunteered.

"Do you really think I could do it? It sounds complicated."

"Of course you can! Come to my place this evening, if you're free, and we'll make a start.

"And don't go bothering to buy any wool; I'm sure to have some odd scraps of yellow and red you can have. I knit a lot, you see."

"Will Rupert take long to make?" Karen dithered.

"Not once you've got the hang of stocking stitch! And, if it looks as though time's running out, I'll give you a hand," Eliza promised. "Well, what do you say?"

"Thanks a lot. I'll give it a try!" Her spirits lifting, Karen smiled and held up the book. "I'll go and pay for this. There's enough left for paints and things."

Eliza glanced at her watch.

"I'd better go. I'm hoping to catch the post office . . ."

"Right. I'll see you later, then," Karen confirmed. "I can't wait to tell Steve. He'll be tickled pink!"

"IT hasn't been such a bad Christmas day, after all, has it?" Karen whispered. She and Steve stood side by side, gazing down at their sleeping son.

"Things have turned out better than we ever dared hope!" Steve draped his arm round her shoulder.

"Take that phone call last Thursday. I never expected to work on the new Riverside estate! There's enough going up there to keep me busy for ages."

"You deserve it." Karen kissed him. "I've a feeling everything will come good again from now on. You'll see!"

She bent forward to pull up Jake's duvet.

"Wasn't he thrilled with his Rupert stuff? Just look at him, cuddling that bear! He's hardly let go of it all day." A lump rose in her throat.

"I'll never ever forget the look on his little face when he first saw it."

Steve nodded.

"It was great. Though I couldn't help laughing when he said Rupert was better than any old Action Man, and could you please knit one for all his friends at playschool!"

Stifling her giggles, Karen straightened up.

"I must remember to tell Eliza Macgregor that when she comes back from Scotland. But for her, I wouldn't have learned how to knit in the first place."

"I suppose you'll be making all sorts of things now." He gathered her into his arms. "What will it be next? Sweaters and cardigans?"

Without waiting for a reply, he kissed her.

"Nothing that big." Her mouth softened and her eyes sparkled mischievously. "Who knows? If all goes well, I might start thinking about knitting some baby clothes.

"After all, isn't it about time Jake had a little brother or sister?" ■

THE early sunshine had been a bit misleading. Combined with the spectacular autumn colours of the trees, it had given everything a warm golden glow.

It was only now, well away from the shelter of her little car, that Jane realised that she should have worn a jacket. A keen wind had sneaked down from the moors. What Gran used to call a lazy wind. The sort that went straight through you, instead of taking the trouble to go round.

But the first cold snap hadn't put people off. On the contrary, there were plenty of cars on the disused race track. Each with a table or two piled high with bits and pieces, odds and ends, boxes of this and that. Amazing things, sometimes.

Jane shivered and pulled up the collar of her jersey. Now that she was here, better go and rummage around. You never quite knew what a car boot sale would yield. Already there were crowds of Saturday morning bargain hunters ambling from stall to stall.

Couples mostly, she thought, with a pang. And just as quickly, she pushed the thought aside.

Dave was gone. Sailed out of her life. Get used to it. The pain would fade — given

Illustration by Mark Viney.

An Offer She

time. One thing was sure — she wouldn't have him back now. Not if he crawled all the way from London on his hands and knees. And a broken heart didn't stop you from getting on with life. There were lots of things you could do on your own. Bargain hunting was one of them.

Every second Wednesday there was an auction of household effects in a converted boathouse down by the river. Anything from spiral staircases to Jacobean fire surrounds and old stoves. Sometimes she went there, dragging Kate, her flatmate, from in front of the television.

By and large though, everything there was usually too expensive, or in huge lots. So, most weekends she came here, weather permitting. Everything here was affordable. Her friends — Kate among them — had accused her of being addicted. Jane just laughed.

Addiction? It wasn't quite that. Though, to be honest, her student days had left her with a healthy respect for ways of stretching limited resources. No, it was the magic of it all that kept her coming back.

by Lisa Granville.

The joy of the completely unexpected, that sudden, breathtaking moment when you saw a neglected, but beautifully carved picture frame — only a few worm holes — going for fifty pence. Or a huge chunk of amethyst, somebody's unwanted gift, being got rid of for a pound. Or the day she'd found Mr Growler, a big old gentleman Teddy, cuddle-worn but a real character. She'd carried him home for a fiver and he now sat in her bedroom chair in her little flat.

uldn't Refuse!

Best of all were the boxes. Any old boxes, as long as they were wooden. Jane spent hours restoring them. It was one way to fill the lonely evenings, mending, painting. Sometimes covering them in découpage — tiny flower pictures cut out of wrapping paper or magazines which she soaked overnight in strong tea to give them an aged look.

Wonderful Christmas presents they would make, filled with little surprises.

The only two she found this morning were on the half empty stall of a man who was already packing up to go. One was too badly damaged. Dry rot, by the look of it. Jane put it down again. The other was very pretty, with hinges and clasp that she suspected were brass.

She gave the owner a quick glance. He was tall, lean and dark-haired. Youngish and quite nice-looking, she supposed. Wearing jeans and a big fisherman's jersey. But, like her, no jacket. Which was perhaps why he was shivering with cold.

He caught her eye and smiled. It was a nice, friendly smile that reached right up to his eyes. But then he did a double take, looked again, almost as if he was looking beyond her outward appearance. And this time the smile reached out towards her, the warm admiration in it thawing her frozen heart just a little.

Jane blinked. It seemed years since anyone had reacted to her like that. She felt herself blushing and couldn't bring herself to return the smile. He came closer.

"Good morning! Interested in the box?"

"Um . . . just wondering what you wanted for it?" Good heavens, he'd flustered her so much that even her voice seemed to have stopped working properly.

"That depends. Make me an offer." There was laughter behind the words.

Jane smiled to herself. After blowing on her cold fingers, she very carefully opened the lid. Inside, it was lined with faded blue velvet. An old hat-pin lay wedged across the base. As she started to ease it out, something underneath grated and moved. A secret compartment. She caught her breath. How exciting! Anything could be hidden in there.

Out of the very corner of her eye, Jane saw that he was still watching her.

"No," she murmured, looking at him from under her lashes, "I've no idea what to offer you. You tell me what you want for it. Then I'll decide if I think it's worth it."

He gave a theatrical sigh. Taking it from her outstretched hand, he regarded the little box with mock seriousness.

"Now this article has a long and important history. It belonged to a tweeny . . ." He peered at her. "You do know what a tweeny was?"

"I think so. Somewhere between a kitchen and parlour maid? A bit of both, maybe?"

"To a tweeny in service in the household of one of the Ladies-in-Waiting to none other than Her Majesty, Queen Victoria . . . Why are you laughing?"

Jane shook her head.

"Oh, really!"

"You don't believe me? I'm wounded. Speak. Come on. A penny for your thought."

She giggled.

"Shouldn't that be thoughts?"

"What! You have more than one? Beauty *and* intelligence! My, my . . ."

"How much for the box?" said Jane, trying to keep a straight face. "It's too cold for this ridiculous conversation."

"I agree. Bitterly cold. And I've had enough. I need to go and find at least a gallon of scalding hot coffee. And toast. Oh, how I need toast." His eyes twinkled down at her. "I'll take one penny for the box. And . . ."

Jane's smile widened.

"A penny. Would that by any chance be the penny you offered me for my thought?"

"Indeed, yes. So we're quits. There you are." He handed her back the box with a flourish. "Now about that thought . . ."

For a few seconds Jane wavered. No. He was too nice for her to take advantage of.

"I can't accept it," she said, uncomfortably. "You see, there's a secret compartment. Under the lining. And I think something's in it. You should see what it is before letting the box out of your hands."

"Really?" He gave it a gentle shake. "So there is." He grinned at her.

"Couldn't you do with a hot drink? We could examine the box together then."

Jane hesitated for a moment, then smiled. After all, what harm could it do? Besides, her fingers were beginning to turn blue.

"All right. Good idea. I'm sure the temperature is dropping."

"PERFECT," he said, when they were finally thawing out over coffee and a mound of hot buttered toast. "Perfect." He looked at her as he said it. And smiled.

"And now," he announced, "to see whether we've made our fortunes today. Fifty-fifty?" She laughed and nodded. He paused. "You know, if we're partners, it might be an idea to know each other's names. I'm Peter. The funny thing is, although I don't know your name, I feel as if I've known you for ages. Does that sound corny?"

"No." Just at this moment, she understood exactly what he meant, but was much too shy to tell him so. "I'm Jane."

Whistling to himself, Peter took out a penknife and carefully levered up the velvet-covered base of the box. Inside was a small leather purse. And inside that was . . .

"A silver shilling! I can't quite make out the date. Victorian, anyway. Well, we've made a small profit on our investment. More coffee?

"There's something else, too!" Right at the bottom of the box was a small square of paper, yellowed with age and cracked on the folds. "A letter, by the look of it."

Hardly daring to breathe, Jane watched as Peter laid it on the table. Traces of copperplate handwriting remained, just a few characters here and there, but the ink had faded so badly that it was illegible. She didn't need to read it to know it was a love letter.

She sighed.

"Sad to think we shall never know her story."

"Whose?"

"The owner of the box. I mean, this was a love letter. Who sent it? Did it all turn out happily? There's no way of knowing."

"Ah, well," he said, "as a matter of fact, I do know. But there's no point in me telling you. You'll just laugh at me again."

Jane looked hard at him. He wasn't smiling now.

"I won't laugh. Promise. As long as you're not making up stories!"

"The box belonged to my great-grandmother. And she really was in service to a Lady-in-Waiting to the old Queen. Not that she ever spoke to her. According to family legend — which means my gran — she had an unhappy love affair. A sailor, I was told."

"Oh," said Jane, thinking of Dave, and his obsession with racing yachts.

"Anyway, Rose came to Devon with the rest of the household servants when the family visited their country estate. That's where she met my great-grandfather. He was a local farmer. They met at a Harvest Supper. When she went back to London, they wrote to each other. I imagine that must be one of his letters."

"So it did end happily. I'm so glad." Jane smoothed out the letter, trying in vain to make out a single word. "But only one letter? Do you have others?"

Steve shook his head.

"Although she went back to London, she didn't stay long. Joseph went after her, determined to bring her back. And he did. You see, one look, and that was it. Just one look. He knew."

He chased the last piece of toast around his plate, then suddenly looked straight at her. Jane was taken aback by what she read in his eyes. It was something like absolute determination mixed with fear and a sort of shyness. Suddenly confused, she jumped to her feet.

"I really must go."

"Oh," he said, "must you? I was rather hoping you might ask me out to dinner."

"What?" Jane couldn't help laughing at him. What a cheek! "Sorry to disappoint you, Peter."

An Offer She Couldn't Refuse!

"Or a drink?" he persisted. "You could take me to the new wine bar in Fore Street. All right then. If you must be conventional, I'll ask you . . ."

"Thanks," said Jane, "but I like my sanity the way it is. Thanks for the coffee. And the box." She turned to go, then turned back and smiled. "And thanks for sharing the story."

Peter followed her to the car.

"I'm almost sure I have a few more boxes in the attic," he said, thoughtfully. "I'll try and get up there one evening this week. Any chance of you coming back next Sunday?"

"I might — especially if it's a fine day. 'Bye!"

But, as the week went on, the weather took a turn for the worse. Each morning the ground was covered with thick frost. The last of the leaves dropped and it was suddenly winter. On Sunday morning, Jane opened one eye, peeped at the grey sky, and turned determinedly over, pulling the duvet more snugly round her.

It was only later, giggling over the Sunday papers with Kate, that she remembered Peter. She felt a little pang of regret for possibly letting him down. He was a nice man, full of blarney, of course, but nice. Still, if he had any sense at all, he would have stayed in bed, too.

On Wednesday, she managed to persuade Kate to accompany her to the auction rooms.

"You never know what you might find," Jane insisted, though Kate wrinkled her nose. "Well, you like old books."

"I like books," said her friend. "And it's true that I buy second-hand ones, but not mouldering old unreadable things full of creepy crawlies. However, I will come and help you look for your precious boxes. But it's positively the last time . . ."

"Thanks," Jane said, not daring to point out that this was precisely what Kate had said last time, and the time before that.

The auction rooms were packed with people muffled up in warm coats and scarves, looking for woodworm and poring over catalogues. Jane and Kate arrived late, leaving only 15 minutes to look round before the bidding started. At first there seemed to be nothing of interest. The sale was mostly composed of very large Victorian furniture. It was Kate who made the find.

"Look, Jane! By the piano."

"What? The sheet music?"

"No — under that. See the three boxes? Your heart's desire!"

"Oh, they're lovely. D'you think that might be rosewood? Kate, this one's inlaid with mother of pearl . . . and this . . . surely this is a Chinese puzzle box. I can't open it. I wonder what it'll go for."

"Lot two-hundred and seventeen. It won't come up until right at the end," said Kate. "Shouldn't think they'll want much for it. Who wants sheet music these days, after all? As for the rest . . . a few old baking tins, a plastic doll with only one arm, and some cutlery that's seen better days. A fiver, maybe."

"Hope so. There are a lot of people here, though."

"Jane, I'm freezing. Let's walk round, keep warm. Maybe find somewhere that sells hot drinks. We can pop back in half an hour and see which lot they're up to."

Two hot chocolates later, the auctioneer had reached Lot 199. The more important articles had been sold, and he was working fast now, probably as anxious to get home as his customers. The room was jampacked. When she heard Lot 216 called, Jane found herself a chair to stand on and hopped up just in time to see the auctioneer's assistant carrying in her Lot.

"Lot two hundred and seventeen," called the auctioneer. "A quantity of valuable sheet music . . ."

Kate sniggered.

"Plus two charming decorative boxes, believed early Victorian, and a small puzzle box of Eastern origin, plus various other items. Shall we start the bidding at twenty pounds? Twenty pounds, anybody?"

Twenty pounds! Jane was appalled. There was a long silence.

"Ten pounds, then?" the auctioneer begged. "Come along, folks, it's a cold night. Some of us are dreaming of hot toddies and warm beds! Who'll bid me ten pounds? The boxes alone must be worth more than that!"

Jane took a deep breath, squeaked, and raised her hand.

"Ten, I'm bid ten. Any advance on ten?"

"Twelve," said a woman clutching a small dog.

"Fourteen," said Jane.

"Fifteen," said a voice, from somewhere in the crowd. Jane frowned.

"Sixteen," she mouthed.

The auctioneer nodded.

"Sixteen, I'm bid." His eyes searched the crowd. "And seventeen, from the gentleman at the back. And is that . . .? Yes, eighteen from the lady in the fur coat."

"Twenty," called Jane, suddenly determined to outbid everyone. They were her boxes. What a cheek! Kate tugged at her coat.

"Jane!"

"What? Stop pulling me!"

"Jane, they're already up to twenty-five pounds . . . Are they really worth that to you?"

"Thirty pounds," said the auctioneer. "Any advance on thirty pounds? No? Going . . . going . . . gone. Sold to the gentleman at the back for thirty pounds. Can we have your name please, sir?"

The crowd started to part as the purchaser moved forward. Jane was just climbing down from her chair when something about the tall figure approaching the desk caught her attention. He had his back to her. She couldn't be sure. Nevertheless, there was something about the turn of that dark head . . .

"Don't be too disappointed," Kate said, giving her a little hug. "Now, please, can we go home?"

"Disappointed isn't quite the word," Jane mused. "Flummoxed, might be."

THE following Sunday was grey and overcast. Jane got up early, dressing herself in several layers of warm clothes. The site was busier than ever and it took her quite a long time to find Peter. He'd arranged his stall out of the wind, against the side of the pavilion, but he was standing up on the steps, scanning the crowd.

"Hi!" His face lit up as she approached. Her heart gave a little sort of lurch of response. She was almost sure the sun came out at that precise moment. "What happened to you last week? I was here."

"Stayed in bed."

"Cruel. Heartless. After all my trouble . . ."

"Scrambling around in your attic?" Jane asked, covering her smile with a fold of woolly scarf. "Poor Peter. Find anything?"

"As a matter of fact, I've got three very nice little boxes for you to look at. A really pretty one with mother of pearl inlay . . ."

"Lovely. I agree. Looks expensive, though. How much?"

"Oooh, let's see. Two pounds?"

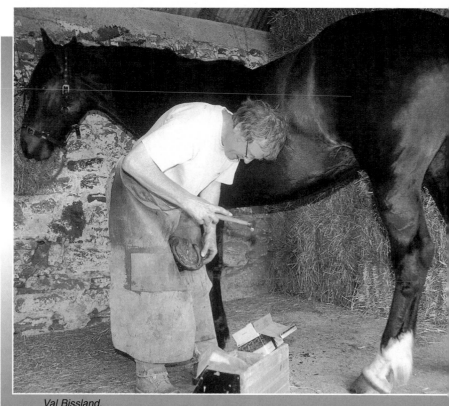

Val Bissland.

"Hmmm. Anything else?"

"Er . . . this one. I think it might be rosewood. That could go for . . . well . . . two pounds as well."

"I see," Jane said. "Well, that's very nice, too. And what about the Chinese puzzle box?"

"I was coming to that." Peter stopped short. He gave her a stunned look. "How did you know that?"

"I was there, Peter. Bidding against you!"

They stared at each other. For a long moment neither said a word. Then Peter began to laugh. Jane shook her head with mock sadness, but his laughter was infectious.

"OK," he said, "so now you know. But when you wouldn't come out with me, I had to do something. I had to see you again. I would have bought all the boxes in the west country, if necessary."

He smiled, his tone was light, but the look in his eyes spoke volumes. Once again Jane felt his warmth touch her wounded heart. And suddenly she knew, without a shadow of doubt, that the healing process was well under way.

The Blacksmith

A SKILFUL man with handsome face,
Descendant of an ancient race,
He knows them all, and understands
Each horse that passes through his hands.

The lady's pure-bred Arab proud,
Its mane and tail a silken cloud;
The farmer's cob, the racehorse slim,
The children's pony, small and trim;
The milkman's nag, the miller's mule,
The mounts from nearby riding school;
The great Shire-horse with feet like plates;
The old grey mare that humbly awaits
A pedicure from trusted friend,
Her working days now at an end.

His soothing voice dispels all fear —
He whispers in a laid-back ear,
Ruffles a mane with brief caress
Of reassuring gentleness,
Then fits the shoe with skill and care,
While passing children stop and stare,
Enraptured by the forge's glow,
The scents and sounds as bellows blow —
Until the smith, his task well done,
Beams on them like the rising sun!
— *Brenda G. Macrow.*

"Breakfast?" he asked. "Same place as last time? Just give me a few minutes to pack this stuff into the car."

They settled down at the same table as before. Jane poured the coffee. Today it smelled wonderful. Even the very ordinary buttered toast was absolutely delicious. It was, she thought, a long time since she'd felt so contented.

"I had to do something," Peter repeated. "Couldn't let you walk out of my life. That's the way it is in my family, Jane. One look, and we know when we've found her."

"Her?" Jane's heart had begun to race as he leaned over and touched her hand. She jumped. Little tingles of electricity ran up her arm.

"You know what I mean."

He was silent for a moment, then, as if he'd said too much, began to tell her about his house — the farmhouse which had been home to Joseph and Rose. It had been sold years ago, when farming was going through the doldrums.

"Lot of work to be done. New thatch, for a start. All very expensive — hence the car boot sales. Of course, most of the land has gone. But then, I'm no farmer. But I swore I'd buy the old place back one day. And I have." He hesitated.

"Jane, I'd really like to show you Heron Farm. It's so beautiful I know you'd love it. And it's not far away. I'm afraid you'd have to follow me — my old jalopy's full of car boot paraphernalia. But we could have lunch in the village pub. Please come."

Jane took a deep breath as their eyes met.

"All right," she said, with a sense of stepping over a threshold into something new and exciting. "Let's go!" ■

Heart

by Mary Kettlewell.

AS they sipped their lemonade in the garden, Celia said she could remember her second birthday spent under the old oak tree.

"You can't possibly, Mum!" her daughter, Mary, protested. "It was over sixty years ago."

"I spent the day sitting up in my pram playing with my new doll — Lulu. The leaves were very green and making a rustling noise in the breeze."

Of Oak

Illustration by Melvyn Warrea-Smith.

"Why do you like the tree so much, Gran?" John, her ten-year-old grandson, asked from where he was sitting on the grass.

She smiled at him affectionately.

After a day in the garden, his knees were black and grazes decorated his elbows.

"You see where those two big branches join together?" She pointed to a fork in the trunk, twenty feet above them. "Your great-grandfather built me a tree-house up there. I spent hours playing in it. I used to have parties for all my toys."

"How did you climb up to it, Gran? There aren't any low branches."

"I had a rope ladder up to that first branch. After that it was easy."

"I didn't know girls could climb like that." John looked at her with admiration.

"Oh, yes! Once I got right up to that high branch — where the jackdaw is perched."

"Mum, will you give me a leg up?" A determined look had formed in John's eyes.

"If your gran could do it, I'm sure you can, John. But take care." She gave him a push up and watched him disappearing into the branches.

"What are those metal things, Gran?" Lois, eleven in a month's time, was pointing to a rusty ring of nails circling the tree.

Celia's face lit up.

"After the war, the whole village had a celebration party in the garden. The vicar let off some fireworks and the American soldiers came along with their band.

"The conductor was such a handsome man." She smiled. "I think he was the first man I ever fell in love with."

"But what were those nails for, Gran?"

"We girls wanted to dance round a maypole — but nobody had a pole! Everything seemed to have disappeared during the war.

"Then the vicar had an idea. Why not use the old oak tree?

"We all raided our mother's sewing boxes and produced lengths of ribbon. Les Cobb, the blacksmith, hammered the ribbons into place and off we danced.

"I've got a photograph of the tree when we'd finished weaving the pattern. I'll show you this evening."

As Lois ran off in pursuit of the family cat, Mary turned to her mother.

"That's not the real reason you love the tree so much, Mum. It's because of Henry, isn't it?"

"I've told you the story so many times, you must be bored stiff." Celia laughed.

"Go on, Mum," Mary urged. "Tell me again. I know you're longing to."

Celia settled herself more comfortably into the deck-chair.

"The funny thing is, it doesn't seem all that long ago. I was just sixteen and Henry was a last-minute invitation to my birthday party. I'd asked Jimmy, who sat next to me in class, but he couldn't come."

"Poor old Henry. Second best! It's a wonder he agreed!"

"Well, he told me later he had a secret crush on me!"

"Go on, Mum. Get to the best part."

"It was after the strawberries and cream. The others went off to stick a tail on the donkey, but Henry had other ideas. He challenged me to climb the oak tree.

"We climbed higher than I'd ever been before and I don't mind telling you I was terrified.

"'Come on, Mary,' Henry kept saying. 'Don't be a chicken.'

"We must have been fifty feet off the ground when he kissed me! I nearly fell off the branch!"

"How romantic! It sounds like something out of Robin Hood."

"It wasn't romantic when I came back down to earth. Your grandmother was livid. My beautiful new party dress was torn and my patent leather shoes were scuffed to pieces. I thought I was going to get the telling off of my life!

"Then Mum looked at my face and smiled. I think she guessed what had happened in the tree and didn't want to spoil it for me."

THERE was a flurry of gravel in the drive and the slam of a car door. Dan, tall and dark-haired, tossed his briefcase on to the back step and gave his wife a kiss.

"Well, thank goodness it's the weekend," he said as he slumped down on an empty deck-chair.

"There's still some tea in the pot." Celia smiled at her son-in-law. "And Mary's made a gorgeous fruit cake."

"So what are you all talking about?" Dan asked, biting into a thick slice.

"Mum's telling me about the time Henry kissed her fifty feet above ground. A highly risky procedure by the sound of it!"

"Did you ever show John and Lois your wedding photos, Celia? With Henry standing under the oak cutting the cake with a sword?" Dan grinned. "It was probably last used by some warring crusader charging into battle on horseback."

Celia was laughing as she explained.

"It actually came from a junk shop on Hampstead Heath. Henry took me courting up by the ponds and, afterwards, we visited this little shop, where we bought the sword.

"After the wedding, Henry hurled the sword at the oak tree. By a complete stroke of luck, it stuck in the bark like a dart. Nobody was more surprised than him."

Celia took Dan by the arm.

"Look, you can still see the cut in the tree."

"So you can." Dan peered at the small scar in the bark.

T HE "Old Rock" captured my heart the moment I disembarked from the ferry. It's a wild land, shrouded in mystery, as well as mist! A visit in summer, however, is rewarded with eighteen hours of daylight — known as the simmer dim.

Though Shetland is as far north as Norway, it's a fertile island, producing fruit and vegetables and a variety of herbs. And, like many of Scotland's islands, it affords an abundance of locally caught fish and shellfish.

You can find the freshest of fish in local restaurants or perhaps enjoy locally-reared lamb. After dinner, I often skipped pudding to concentrate on cheese and oatcakes. Oatcakes are something of a local speciality and my real weakness.

If you enjoy homebaking, like me, you'll find the town of Lerwick is the place to go. The bakery there produces a variety of cakes, breads and oatcakes, and the frequent Women's Institute fêtes offer a seemingly endless array of home-baked goodies, made from old family recipes.

Lerwick is also home to the Shetland Smokehouse, which produces a wide range of smoked and marinated fish, delicious pâtés and interesting soups — just the thing for cooler days. And it's certainly easy to put together a gourmet's picnic, too!

Enjoying a meal out in Shetland, you may be surprised to be offered a White Wife or Auld Rock. These are both local beers, brewed and bottled at the Valhalla Brewery, the most northerly brewery in

Salmon smoking.

A Taste O'

"I love that tree." Celia sighed. "It's full of memories . . . almost like a living history book . . ."

*   *   *   *

One night the following March, there was a howling gale. Next morning, Celia looked out of her window to find that a large bough had broken away from the oak tree.

"It'll have to come down, I'm afraid, Mrs Jesson," the tree surgeon told her. "The trunk looks all right from the outside, but it's rotten at the base."

"But you can't cut it down!" Celia was close to tears. "It's hundreds of years old. I played in it when I was a little girl and my . . . my husband first . . . well, when we married our reception was under its branches."

But there was nothing else for it and, when she signed the piece of paper authorising the felling, Celia's hand was shaking.

Shetland

Tranquil Shetland coastline.

Gordon Henderson.

Britain. Auld Rock is a common nickname for Shetland and White Wife is named after a local ghost!

While on Shetland, I did do some of my own catering, as I was camping. I was spoilt for choice when buying local produce and enjoyed many delicious picnics. I was even lucky enough to acquire some duck eggs from a friendly farmer.

The problem was — how would I cook the eggs? Shetland is flat and treeless, so finding even the smallest piece of wood to make my fire proved a Herculean task! I'll be sure to remember to pack a wee gas stove for my next trip!

Valhalla Beers.

"Mum! What's the matter?" Mary asked when the family called round that evening.

"The oak tree has got to come down, Mary. It's rotten inside."

"Gran, don't be sad." Lois threw her arms round her. "You've still got us."

"There's an oak tree in Hobbitt's wood just as big as this one. I'll show you. You could give me a leg up and watch me climb it." John tried to console her, too. "I expect Grandad played in it when he was a boy . . ."

"It's Mothering Sunday next week," Dan said as they left. "Why don't we all think of a present for Celia? Something to do with trees."

Everyone agreed it was a good idea.

Lois counted out all her pocket money and, with a bit of help from her dad, found that she had enough to buy a small bonsai tree.

John shut himself up in his bedroom for three hours with a hammer and nails and emerged with a rather rickety "tree" that he had knocked

171

together from pieces of scrap wood.

Mary and Dan took a trip to the nursery and purchased a sapling oak.

On Mother's Day, the family arrived at Celia's to find the oak had been completely removed. And Celia was making a great effort to be cheerful.

"We've brought this for you, Celia," Dan said, unwrapping the sapling. He set the spindly little tree in its protective wrapping down on the sitting-room carpet.

"You've all been so kind!" Celia was fighting back tears. "The presents are lovely."

She turned to Dan.

"Will you help me plant it this evening? I'd like to think there's still an oak growing in the garden even though the big one's gone."

The children were fast asleep in the back of the car on the drive home, when Dan had his idea.

"It's brilliant!" Mary enthused. "I wish I'd thought of it."

"I'll go round first thing tomorrow and see what the tree surgeon has got to say."

The following morning, Dan reported back to Mary.

"Luckily, Alan's still got the wood. And he knows a man who can do the job. It'll take a while though."

"But they'll be finished by Mum's birthday?"

Dan sighed.

"He said they'd do their best, but even with fast modern methods of seasoning, it'll be awfully tight. And it'll cost a bit."

"We'll survive." Mary smiled.

THE day of Celia's birthday — June the twentieth — was a glorious summer day.

"Don't say anything yet," Mary whispered to the children as they arrived. "We'll leave the surprise till the last minute."

"Happy birthday, Gran," Lois said. "Here's your present." She looked at her grandmother shyly. "Can I watch while you open it?"

She had made Celia a pair of oven gloves and had very cleverly tracked down some colourful material patterned with tiny trees.

"Darling, they're just what I wanted." Celia ruffled Lois's hair. "My old ones are threadbare. I burnt my finger only yesterday."

John produced his parcel from behind his back with a grin.

"It's a joke, Gran!"

Celia pulled off the paper. Inside was a pottery hippopotamus, wearing a hat, a pair of miniature spectacles, four tiny boots and a colourful tie.

"I thought it'd make you laugh, Gran."

"What a lovely present, John, love. I can't think of anything I'd like better."

Dan put his arm round Celia's shoulders.

"Now, Gran, there's a present from all of us on its way. We've just got to go and fetch it. Come on, kids." The entire family disappeared in the direction of the front drive.

Five minutes later, they reappeared. John and Lois were carrying two rustic chairs apiece and Dan and Mary were staggering under the weight of the garden table.

"There." Dan put the table down with a sigh. "It's come back."

"Come back?" Celia looked puzzled.

"It's the old oak tree, Gran," Lois explained, "turned it into garden furniture for you."

"We thought you'd like to see it in the garden again, Mum." Mary took her mother's hand. "It's the tree's rightful home."

"It's the most wonderful birthday present I could possibly have. I can't thank you all enough."

Dan pointed to a small notch in one of the table's legs.

"That's where Henry's sword stuck in!"

Mary ran her hand over the surface.

"And those bits come from the topmost fork, where you and Grandad first kissed. We had a terrible job finding the right piece."

"Do you really like it, Gran?" the children asked in unison, longing to share in her excitement.

"Like it? It's made my day."

They placed the cake in the centre of the table.

"There's only thirty-two candles, Gran." Lois was dancing round the table. "We couldn't fit sixty-four on!"

"Each one stands for two years," John added.

"We must keep to the old family tradition," Dan said, producing the old sword. "Who's going to cut the first slice?"

$$* \quad * \quad * \quad *$$

Much later, when everyone had gone home, Celia ventured back into the garden.

The moon was shining down on the table, turning it into a soft yellow.

Celia placed her finger on the scar where the sword had once been.

"Welcome home, Henry, love. I've missed you."

As Celia wandered indoors, a gentle breeze seemed to come from nowhere, causing the leaves on the little evergreen oak sapling to rustle as if in reply, "it's good to be back." ∎

ISBN 0-85116-7373
EAN 9-780851-167374

Killybegs Coastline, Donegal

MANY a fishing boat has crossed these waters, heading for Killybegs, one of Northern Ireland's major fishing harbours. This is a fascinating part of Ireland and was once home to noteable carpet factory which supplied rugs to Buckingham Palace, The White House and The Vatican.

Nowadays tourists are assured a warm Irish welcome and many come to take part in the annual sea angling festival, or simply to soak up the scenery.